ChiWalking Workbook

Your Step-by-step, 8-week Guide to Developing a ChiWalking Program

Katherine and Danny Dreyer

Also by Danny and Katherine Dreyer: ChiRunning

ChiLiving, Inc.
530 Merrimon Avenue
Suite A
Asheville, NC 28804

Designed by Karen Soleau
Illustrations ©2006 by Karen Soleau

Cover photograph by Lori Cheung © 2005 The PortraitPhotographer.com

www.chiliving.com

CONTENTS

WELCOME TO THE CHIWALKING WORKBOOK

By starting this program you're opening up the door to better health, increased energy and joy in your life.

The ChiWalking program will show you how to maximize the benefits of your walking program. By using the ChiWalking method, you'll be walking in a way that taps into energy that is already stored in your body. And, you'll be taking full advantage of the energy all around you by using gravity as an ally in your forward movement. By following the Five Mindful Steps you'll discover a way to move that will keep you vibrant and healthy for a lifetime.

GETTING STARTED

This workbook is a companion to the ChiWalking DVD and/or the ChiWalking book: *The Five Mindful Steps for Lifelong Health and Energy* (referred to as "the book" throughout the rest of this workbook). You can use either or both with this workbook.

Throughout this workbook, we'll refer you to sections of the DVD or the book. The DVD provides the best visual demonstrations and support to learning this technique. We do suggest you watch the DVD in its entirety first, to give you an overview of the program, or, if you prefer, just start with Lesson I on the DVD. If you prefer to have a thorough understanding of the underlying principles of ChiWalking, we suggest reading the book. Each week you will learn a Lesson from the DVD (or the book), Take your time practicing each Lesson and then enjoy your walk.

Please read this entire introduction for health and safety reasons.

SETTING ASIDE TIME

The first week of this Eight-week Program asks for you to devote three, 50-minute workouts to your walking program. You won't be walking the whole time. The walks for the first several weeks are 15-25 minutes. The program includes doing pre-walk Body Looseners and post-walk Stretches that are as important to your health and well-being as the walks themselves. You'll also be creating your own program so that at the end of the eight weeks you'll have a plan to last you a lifetime.

As the weeks progress we begin to increase the length and number of workouts, so that by week eight, you're up to five, one-hour workouts. Walking is such a safe way to get fit that you can walk seven days a week. If this walking program is your primary fitness activity, we recommend that you eventually build up to and walk at least five days a week in order to reap the full rewards.

The important part is to set aside the time, and make your health, and your workouts a priority. Eventually, your walking program will become a natural part of your every day life.

Please use caution and be sure to consult with a health care practitioner before starting any physical fitness program. If you have any current mitigating health-related factors that you should consider as you begin a regular exercise program, make an appointment to see your health care practitioner. Be sure to share your intentions and goals with your practitioner, and get a thorough physical. Don't be afraid to ask questions or address any major health issues you may have.

INCLUDE CHIWALKING AS PART OF YOUR FITNESS PROGRAM

If you already have a regular walking or fitness routine, you can include the ChiWalking method in your current program. The goal of this workbook is to take your fitness to a new level by focusing on the quality of your workouts by incorporating the ChiWalking techniques. We suggest you practice the ChiWalking method for a minimum of the workout times recommended in order to learn these new skills. If you're getting ready for a walking event, especially a distance event such as a 10k or half marathon, you can use this workbook to incorporate the ChiWalking method into your training. We want to help you make safe, optimal moving habits a part of everything you do.

Take your time and deeply incorporate the skills in the first few weeks of this program into your current regime. As we tell all our students, "take your time, and you'll learn more quickly".

FORM FIRST, QUALITY-NOT QUANTITY

If health is your goal, mindful movement is the key. In ChiWalking what is most important is the quality of your workouts, not the quantity. It starts by focusing on your Form First. When you're just beginning your ChiWalking program, the distance you cover is not as important as the length of time you can walk using the ChiWalking method. In other words, it is better for your overall health and well-being to walk for 30 minutes, mindfully, Body Sensing (listening to your body) and with good walking form, than walking for 45 minutes with poor habits. When you consciously direct your energy with the form techniques in this workbook, the long-term benefits are far reaching. Just remember: Form First.

GRADUAL PROGRESS – BE KIND TO YOURSELF

One of the key principles of ChiWalking is Gradual Progress. It is also the key to allowing for the time and space to learn something new. Gradual Progress (pg. 62 of the book) is all about the natural progression of growth. Everything starts small and takes time to grow. In our instant gratification society, we don't allow time for things to progress naturally. When we do, beautiful things happen. It is also a way to remember to be gentle with yourself. We tend to expect too much of ourselves and then give up easily if we don't get something right away. Gradual Progress asks you to allow yourself to be a beginner again, to be the seed of your potential, to discover the fun of learning something new.

Take your time with ChiWalking. Enjoy it. Whether you're learning to swivel your hips or walk with a new rhythm, relax, enjoy, and have fun. It is the best way to learn and the best way to enjoy life.

WALK WITH A FRIEND

Having a walking companion who is also practicing the ChiWalking program is a wonderful idea. You're more likely to stay committed to a routine when you've got someone else relying on your companionship! And, you can help teach each other the form focuses. You can find a partner at the ChiWalking website (www.chiwalking.com) by going to the Community Bulletin Board.

THE FIVE MINDFUL STEPS

1. Get Aligned

2. Engage Your Core

3. Create Balance

4. Make a Choice

5. Move Forward

TIPS FOR FINDING THE TIME

Because humans are creatures of habit, once you establish a routine of walking (which is what we're going to do in the next eight weeks) it will be easy and quite automatic to "make the time to walk." Here are a few suggestions:

• Aim to walk every other day, minimally.

• Try to walk at the same time on the same day.

• Go to bed early so you can get up earlier the next morning for "you" time. Place your walking shoes right beside your bed.

• Use your lunchtime to go for a walk.

• Set aside time after dinner, making an after-dinner walk as much a ritual as the meal.

• Be mindful of time wasted doing unnecessary activities like watching TV. Skip a television show and go for a walk instead.

HELPING YOU TO CREATE TIME FOR YOURSELF

If it's difficult for you to make time for yourself, here is an exercise to help you. Read the following suggestions, and then fill in the blanks:

Shift Your Mindset to Take Good Care of Yourself

"I'm tired." _____

"Once I get moving, I'll feel energized and great."

"I've got too much to do." _____

"I'll go for a walk and think about how I can better prioritize my most important tasks and minimize the minor ones."

"I don't feel up to it today." _____

"I might not feel up for it tomorrow, either. But I know ChiWalking will change my mood in an instant."

"I just ate and just want to watch TV." _____

"A walk will help my digestion and I'll feel more physically relaxed and spiritually energized afterwards."

"I'll do it tomorrow." _____

"Why wait to feel great?"

Write down your biggest challenges or excuses:_____

_____

_____

_____

_____

_____

Now write down how you can conquer them by shifting your mindset:_____

_____

_____

_____

_____

TRAINING TOOLS AND EQUIPMENT

Recommended Equipment: (pages 67-70 in the book)

• Walking Shoes: Your shoes are very important and should be comfortable, roomy and flexible. For more information refer to the book, pg 69 or visit, www.chiwalking.com.

• Countdown Timer: A sport watch with a repeat countdown timer is very helpful. We'll start using a countdown timer in Week One. If you don't have a sport watch, use any kind of a countdown timer that you can carry with you.

• Small metronome: Like a fine musician, a metronome will help you find your natural rhythm and is one of the best training tools there is. We'll start using it in Week Five. (The best one we've found is available at www.ChiWalking.com).

Additional Equipment: *(but not entirely necessary for this program)*

• Pedometer: Our pedometer will count your steps, tell you how far and how many minutes you've walked, how many calories you've burned, and even give you the time of day. It is not necessary to help you learn the ChiWalking method, but it's a great way to keep track of your progress. (Available at www.chiwalking.com)

• Heart rate monitor: We don't use them for this program, and we recommend you learn to take your pulse. However for some people, a heart rate monitor is a helpful tool to keep at an optimal heart rate range.

Where to Walk

For the first few weeks find easy, flat terrain on which to walk. You can't learn this form properly on hills. This could mean you simply do your workouts in your neighborhood, or better yet, on a nearby track. Do what works for you. Later on, we'll suggest when to add hills, trails, or increase the intensity of your workouts by testing out new terrain. It is fine if you need to walk on a treadmill, however, walking on a treadmill is different than walking on a non-moving surface. Make sure you read the section on treadmill walking in the book, (pg. 220).

Safety First

The first rule is to be safe. Whether you're walking by yourself, or walking further than you're used to, or doing your workouts at night or in the early morning, the most important thing is your safety. Listening to the ChiWalking audio program and walking on busy city streets may not be the best idea. Be smart. Listen to your instincts. Plan your walking routes. Walk with a friend. Walk on a treadmill. Take good care of yourself.

HOW TO USE THIS WORKBOOK

In addition to getting out those walking shoes and lacing up, we want you to get out your pens, open your minds, and be ready to use this workbook for what it's intended: as a workbook! That means you're free to write, earmark, and doodle as much as you like on these pages. Make this your journal for the next eight weeks—your notebook that records thoughts, feelings, goals, personal plans, progress, frustrations, set backs. Use it to chart routes, personal accomplishments and programs, and it will become your friend in this new journey.

THE WEEKLY FORMAT

Each week will follow a similar format. You'll get an overview of the week ahead followed by the Theme of the Week, in which you'll get an overview of the Form Focuses you'll be practicing in the week's walks.

Every week you'll be a student of a Chi-Skill or Chi-Principle. You can observe that skill, or principle, as it works throughout your life, not just in your walking.

In the first workout of every week, you'll be reviewing the ChiWalking Form Focuses for that week in the book or the DVD. In your first lesson, you'll also be practicing the Body Looseners and the Stretches for that week. You'll be adding in the Body Looseners and Stretches cumulatively, so every week, you'll add in one or two more to your routine. If you have the time, definitely learn the looseners and stretches in advance and do them whenever you can.

We always start a ChiWalking workout with loosening. This is a time to relax, feel your body, feel where you are tight, and begin to let go of that tension. We stretch after we walk to keep our muscles limber.

After every walk we have a space in the workbook for your End of Walk Review. For the first several weeks, we ask you some questions, but as time goes on you'll begin to create your own journal. Take the time to jot down some notes. The action of writing down your experience will help deepen it, and your ChiWalking practice will become a more integral part of your life.

At the end of your second weekly-workout we'll have you work on Program Development. Program Development is all about creating a fitness routine that really works for you. We start in Week One by creating a Vision, then in Week Two doing a Personal Assessment, and then Creating Goals in Week Three. By the end of the eight weeks, you'll have crafted a Personal Fitness Program that takes into account all of you–body, mind and spirit. By the end of your eight-week program, you'll have the skills to upgrade your own training program as your needs change. This will help you stay on track to truly create lifelong health and energy.

We always suggest doing your workout first and then doing your Program Development. The physical activity will unleash your creativity and get your mind and spirit open and clear.

We've put all the pages for your Program Development in the back of the book for easy reference, reading and revising. Your Program is for you to create and recreate as the process unfolds.

A LIFELONG PRACTICE

Congratulations. By picking up this workbook you're already on your way to implementing a walking program that will reward you in more ways than one.

The ChiWalking experience is a process and an ongoing practice. It is here to help you manage your energy and your health. At the end of eight weeks you'll have a solid program in place and a set of tools that can keep you walking for a lifetime.

ChiWalking unlocks the hidden potential in walking by exploring all of its vast possibilities. With ChiWalking, you'll get into great physical shape, strengthen your life force, increase your energy and be inspired for a lifetime.

LET'S GET GOING!

Did You Know?

• *Taking 10,000 steps a day will not only keep you fit but, if your daily caloric intake remains constant, you can lose up to a pound a week.*

• *A brisk thirty-minute walk, just three times a week, has been shown to be just as effective as anti-depressant medication in relieving the symptoms of major depression in middle-aged and elderly people.*

• *2-1/2 hours or more of walking per week, in combination with a healthier diet, did more to ward off diabetes than did a popular diabetes-prevention drug.*

WEEK 1 OVERVIEW

Theme of the Week: Get Aligned

Chi-Skill: Focusing
• Making ChiWalking a mindful practice
• Using a watch with a count down timer

Minimum Time Commitment: 3 x 50-minute workouts, 2.5 hours total

Body Looseners: ankles, knees

3 Walks: Easy comfortable pace on smooth and flat terrain
         Total walking time: 15-20 minutes per walk (or longer if you want)

Post Walk Stretches: calf stretch, achilles stretch
(Appendix B, pg. 189 in this workbook.)

Program Development: Create and Write a Vision

What to re-read in the book: Chapter 2: Step 1. Get Aligned • Step 2. Engage Your Core • Step 3. Create Balance *(pages 21-34)* • Chapter 4: Align Yourself and Engage Your Core *(pages 72-82)*.

What to re-view on DVD: Lesson One: The Three Steps to Create Great Posture. Watch the DVD on the first workout of this week, and if you want to, also at the start of your second and third workouts for reinforcement.

Write in the days and times for your 3 sessions this week:

Workout #1	Workout #2	Workout #3
Day _____	Day _____	Day _____
Time _____	Time _____	Time _____

THEME OF THE WEEK

Get Aligned: Be Mindful of Your Posture Every Step of the Way

Proper alignment of your posture, takes center stage during this first week. For everyone, beginners and seasoned walkers alike, the most important component of your walking practice is your posture. We'll be working on some aspect of posture in almost every work-out, but let's practice getting it right from the start.

What's so important about maintaining alignment? Good alignment allows Chi—your life force—to flow naturally and freely, like a stream of energy through your body. The Chi-Principle of Cotton and Steel (page 23 of the book) explains this idea well. Having great structural alignment with a straight spinal column (your needle) will allow your structure, not your muscles, to support your body weight. Then, as you relax everything (the cotton) around your column, such as your shoulders, arms, hips, and legs, the core muscles of your body will be set to work and your arms and legs can take a back seat.

> *You're learning to walk from core strength—not leg strength!*

As you practice strengthening your core muscles, you'll begin to sense an "inner strength" developing, which you can tap into anytime in your daily life. It's truly a wonderful feeling!

Before every walk this week, practice the one-legged posture stance *(see page 83 of the book for instructions or Lesson 1 of the DVD)*. Notice the difference in how it feels when your pelvis is level and when it's not. As you move from one foot to the other, feel a straight line running from your head to your toe.

As you start walking, the first thing you should do is *pretend you're not walking*. That's right. Instead, just imagine that every time your foot hits the ground, you are doing a one-legged posture stance. Just go for as long as you're comfortable. If it's only for 5 or 10 minutes, that's okay. Remember, you're going to be building upon your skills as well as your strength and cardio-capacity. If you can complete three 20-minute walks this week, great, but don't worry if you need to take it more slowly and add minutes farther along in your program. This is YOUR program. Be patient with yourself and you will succeed.

If you're a seasoned walker, practice your new ChiWalking skills at intervals during your walks. Practice for 15 minutes, then give yourself a 2-5 minute break, then practice your posture again for 15 minutes. Alternate back and forth in this way, and try to practice the focuses for the majority of your walk.

When your posture is aligned properly, your body weight is supported by your bones, ligaments, and tendons (not your muscles). This will significantly reduce your workload while walking.

CHI-SKILL OF THE WEEK

Focusing

This week we're going to pay attention to: Focusing. It is one of the five Chi-Skills detailed in Chapter 3 of the book (pages 41 to 43).

The practice of focusing keeps you headed toward your immediate goals and, in the greater scheme of life, towards realizing your bigger vision. Focusing exercises your brain. In ChiWalking, your mind gets a workout by first scanning your body, then by directing your body with a Form Focus and then listening to the response. But you'll also find that throughout your workout, your mind will wander. I guarantee it! You'll start thinking about work, stressing about a to-do list, or planning for the upcoming week. This mental wandering happens naturally. It takes practice to learn how to hold your attention to one task only, such as focusing on your alignment or leveling your pelvis. Learning to focus is really learning to re-focus your mind, over and over again.

A watch with a repeating countdown timer comes in handy for helping your mind remain focused, which is why we'll be introducing its use starting this first week. We highly recommend getting a sports watch with a countdown timer. (The Timex Ironman watch has an excellent countdown timer.) Get to know your watch and how to program it to sound at certain intervals. Or, just use a kitchen timer. With every walk you'll be focusing on different aspects of your form. By the end of the eight weeks, you'll be a skilled at focusing your mind, and that will be an asset you can carry over into every aspect of your life! A focused mind is the key to making any activity a mindful practice.

WORKOUT #1

Today's Date: _____

Before beginning your first ChiWalking workout, pause for a moment, and think about the eight weeks ahead of you. Visualize what it will be like to be out there walking regularly. Imagine what your world will be like with a regular fitness program.

LESSON: 15 MINUTES

Take the time to review the following materials in the book and practice along with the DVD to learn how to create great posture .

• Review Lesson 1 on the DVD: 15 Minutes

• Review the ChiWalking text, pages 72-100

PRE-WALK BODY LOOSENERS: 5 Minutes

These exercises will relax your muscles and loosen your joints so that your walking will be more fluid. *(Refer to the book, pages 142-143 for more info, and watch the DVD section on "Body Looseners".)*

Begin by shaking out your whole body like you're a rag doll, especially your arms and legs. Feel your head, neck, shoulders, arms, hands, torso, abdomen, legs, and feet cut loose. Really shake and let it all go!

Then, do the following exercises:

• **Ankle rolls:** Do 10 clockwise circles and then 10 counter-clockwise circles. Switch legs and repeat the exercise.

• **Knee Circles:** Do 10 clockwise circles and then 10 counter-clockwise circles.

Shake out that body again. Begin to FEEL your physical being from the top of your head all the way down to your toes.

Learn Post-Walk Stretches: *5 Minutes*
• Review your post-walk stretches now so that you can transition directly into stretching upon return. Refer to Appendix B page 189 in this workbook to review the **Calf Stretch** and **Achilles Stretch**.

MOVE FORWARD INTO YOUR WALK: 15-20 minutes

You're about to step outside (or on the treadmill) and do a walk. If you can go for more than 15 minutes, do it! If not, that's okay. This is your first day so take it slowly and go at your own pace. Use your watch to divide your walk into three, 5-minute intervals. (Set it to beep every five minutes.) This will remind you to shift your thinking to a new form focus —and help to make sure you're still mindful of the walk itself!

FOCUSES DURING THE WALK

• First 5 minutes: **one-legged posture stance**. Imagine that every time your foot hits the ground, you're doing a one-legged posture stance.

• Second 5 minutes: **feeling the ground** with your feet as you extend through the top your head.

• Last 5 minutes: Focus on both, the **one-legged posture stance** and **feeling the**

straight line as you extend through the top of your head.

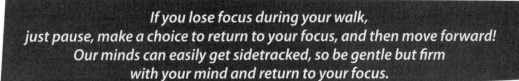

If you lose focus during your walk,
just pause, make a choice to return to your focus, and then move forward!
Our minds can easily get sidetracked, so be gentle but firm
with your mind and return to your focus.

POST WALK STRETCHES: 5 Minutes

Do your **calf** and **achilles** stretches.

✳ SEE YOU WHEN YOU GET BACK! ✳

END OF WALK REVIEW: 5 Minutes

Hurray! By now you should have completed your walk and your post-walk stretches, and you might feel different than you did at the start of this first session. Now it's time to devote these last 5 minute to jotting down a few personal notes.

How did you feel after your walk? _____

_____

_____

_____

_____

How many minutes did you walk?_____

How well were you able to keep your posture aligned while walking?

_____

_____

Were there any posture focuses you had trouble doing or remembering? If so, which ones? *(Pay attention to these all week or until they no longer present a difficulty. Highlight your trouble spots here!)* _____

_____

_____

_____

_____

Could you sense in your body when it was time to stop walking? _____

Is there anything you learned during today's walk? (Any realizations or understandings?) What were they?_____

_____

_____

_____

_____

_____

FOCUSES IN BETWEEN WORKOUTS

The best way to prepare for your next workout and continue to build upon your program is to pay attention to your body throughout the day. For this entire week, make it a point to focus on:

• Posture alignment

• Needle in Cotton—feeling your column engaged while relaxing everything else in your body.

You can do these focuses just about anywhere, no matter what you're doing; cooking, cleaning, driving, shopping, even pumping gas into your car! So here's what you're going to do, choose at least two times a day to remember your posture:

• When you first get out of bed.

• When you get up out of your desk chair.

• When you get out of the car.

• When you prepare a meal in the kitchen.

• Standing in front of the mirror before bed.

Think about what you do routinely every day and then take an extra minute during that time to make a conscious effort and practice. Record here when those times will be:

_____ and _____

Those extra minutes every day will make you feel wonderful, and you'll be all the more prepared for your next session.

RE-NEW YOUR COMMITMENT

I will do another ChiWalking session on this day:_____
(Write this date down on your calendar or in any daily planner you keep.)

WORKOUT #2

Today's Date: _____

LESSON: 5 MINUTES

• Practice getting into great posture *(Review the Posture Lesson on the DVD)*

RE-CAP The four key steps to proper alignment are:

1.   **Align** your feet.

2.   **Lengthen** your upper spine.

3.   **Level** your pelvis.

4.   **Tilt** your statue 1/4" forward from the hips.

When you have aligned your posture, have a friend pull down on your shoulders, and feel the difference. Your body should feel like a tree trunk—strong and solid.

PRE-WALK BODY LOOSENERS: 5 Minutes

Refer to the Body Looseners on the DVD or pages 142-143 in the book.

• Shake out your entire body from head to toe. Let loose!

• Then do your **ankle rolls** and **knee circles**.

Take a moment to FEEL every square inch of your body. Shake it out again if you like!

Review Post-Walk Stretches: *5 minutes*
If necessary refer to Appendix B to review the **calf stretch** and **achilles stretch**.

MOVE FORWARD INTO YOUR WALK: 15-20 minutes

Aim to walk for 15 minutes if you didn't reach that length of time in your first workout. (Again, don't let anything stop you from going for a longer walk if you feel up to it!) Instead of setting your watch to go off every 5 minutes, set it to repeat at *one-minute intervals*. Use the beep as a reminder to reinstate whichever focus you're working on. This will train your mind to focus by bringing it back from La-La Land at least once every minute.

FOCUSES DURING THE WALK

• First 2 minutes: **one-legged posture stance**. Imagine that every time your foot hits the ground, you're doing a one-legged posture stance.

• Second 8 minutes: Walk with your **feet pointing forward.** (Don't let your feet turn out!)

• Last 5 minutes: Maintain both focuses at the same time -- the **one-legged posture stance** and **pointing your feet forward** by rotating your entire leg in toward your centerline.

Staying focused is a huge challenge for anyone. We're going to use the watch as a tool today to periodically refocus ourselves and remain mindful every step of the way. When you hear your watch sound, take note of your posture, bring your mind back into focus, and then review either your one-legged posture stance and/or your column. See if you can hold your focus for an entire minute! It's harder than you think.

POST WALK STRETCHES: 5 Minutes

Do your **calf** and **achilles** stretches.

✳ SEE YOU WHEN YOU GET BACK! ✳

END OF WALK REVIEW: 5 Minutes

By now you have completed your walk and your post-walk stretches. You might feel a bit different than you did at the start of this workout. Keeping track of how you feel throughout your progress is a powerful tool, so devote these last 5 minutes to jotting down a few personal notes.

How did you feel after your walk? _____

_____

_____

_____

How many minutes did you walk?

_____

How well were you able to keep your posture aligned while walking?

_____

Were there any posture focuses you had trouble doing or remembering? If so, which ones?

_____

_____

_____

Could you sense in your body when it was time to stop walking?

_____

_____

_____

Is there anything you learned during today's walk? (Any realizations or understandings?) What were they?

_____

_____

_____

_____

PROGRAM DEVELOPMENT: 10 Minutes

Create a Vision (***Go to Appendix A, Chapter 1, Part 1)***
(Refer to pages 182 and 183 in the book for more information on Creating a Vision.)

FOCUSES IN BETWEEN WORKOUTS

Don't forget! Pay attention to your **posture** between now and your next workout. If you've had a difficult time remembering to practice your posture twice a day, Make a Choice to renew your commitment now. Choose two new times during the day when you are most likely to straighten up.

I'll practice my posture at these times during the day:

_____ and _____

RE-NEW YOUR COMMITMENT

I will do another ChiWalking session on this day:_____
(Write this date down on your calendar or in any daily planner you keep.)

WORKOUT #3

Today's Date: _____

LESSON: 5 MINUTES

• Practice **one-legged posture stance**: *5 Minutes*

Before walking today, spend 5 minutes doing one-legged posture stances on your right and left legs. Use the DVD for guidance if you need to.

(In T'ai Chi class we start every session with practicing our posture. Getting aligned for your walking will help you get aligned with your potential.)

RE-CAP   The four key steps to proper alignment are:

1.   **Align** your feet.

2.   **Lengthen** your upper spine.

3.   **Leve**l your pelvis.

4.   **Tilt** your statue 1/4" forward from the hips.

Memorize this feeling and bring it with you on every step of your walk!

PRE-WALK BODY LOOSENERS: 3 Minutes

(Refer to "Body Looseners" on the DVD or pages 142-143 of the book.)

• Shake out your entire body from head to toe. Let loose!

• Do your ankle rolls and knee circles.

> *Take a moment to FEEL every square inch of your body.*
> *Inhale a big, deep breath that fills your lungs from the bottom up and pushes your*
> *belly out. Then, exhale completely, relaxing your chest first.*
> *FEEL your body once more. Shake it again if you like!*

MOVE FORWARD INTO YOUR WALK: 20 minutes

Set your countdown timer to five-minute intervals.
Do each focus for 5 minutes .

FOCUSES DURING THE WALK

• First 5 minutes: **One-legged posture stance**. Imagine that every time your foot hits the ground, you're doing a one-legged posture stance.

• Second 5 minutes: **Feeling the ground** with your feet as you extend through the top of your head.

• Next 10 minutes: **Open up your chest** and lengthen your upper body.

• Final 5 minutes: Concentrate on all three focuses simultaneously. They all work in synergy. Feel the ground. Then feel the energy come up through your feet, legs, spine (column), and up through the top of your head. Tuck your chin, open your chest, and extend your upper body. Point your feet forward.

POST WALK STRETCHES: 5 Minutes

Do your **calf** and **achilles** stretches.

✳ SEE YOU WHEN YOU GET BACK! ✳

END OF WALK REVIEW: 5 Minutes

Evaluate your experience as you did in your previous sessions.

How did you feel after your walk? _____

_____

_____

_____

Could you sense in your body when it was time to stop walking?

_____

_____

_____

_____

How many minutes did you walk?

_____

How well were you able to keep your posture aligned while walking?
Well? So-so? Not well?

_____

_____

Were there any posture focuses you had trouble doing or remembering? If so, which ones?

_____

_____

_____

Is there anything you learned during today's walk? (Any realizations or understandings?)
What were they?

_____

_____

_____

_____

PROGRAM DEVELOPMENT: 10 Minutes

Review and refine your Vision
Go to Appendix A: Chapter 1, Part 2

Congratulations on finishing Week 1. Take a minute and remember to sense how good you felt during and after walking.
Focus on the positive and feel the goodness happening to your body. Remember, ChiWalking is a process.
With the first week done, you have a great foundation from which to create great health and well-being.

RE-NEW YOUR COMMITMENT

I will start Week 2 on this day:_____
(Write this date down on your calendar or in any daily planner you keep.)

WEEK 2 OVERVIEW

Theme of the Week: Engage your core and create balance!

Chi-Principle: Gradual Progress
  • Relishing the process

Minimum Time Commitment: 3 x 50-minute workouts, 2.5 hours total

Body Looseners: ankles - knees - **hips**

3 Walks: Smooth and flat terrain – Core strength awareness and creating balance
  1. 20-minute walking test at a faster pace than usual
  2. 15-20 minute walk at an easy, comfortable pace
  3. 15-20 minute walk at an easy, comfortable pace

Post Walk Stretches: (Appendix B pg. 189)
Calf stretch, achilles stretch, **hip flexor stretch**, **hamstring stretch**

Program Development: Personal Assessment: Physical, Mental

What to re-read in the book: Chapter 2, "Engage Your Core" and "Create Balance", pages 26-34; Chapter 4, pages 62-82; and Chapter 7, pages 184-191.

What to re-view on DVD: Lesson One: The Three Steps to Create Great Posture.

Watch the DVD before the first session this week, then, if necessary, at the start of your second and third session for reinforcement.

Write in the days and times for your 3 sessions this week:

Workout #1	**Workout #2**	**Workout #3**
Day _____	Day _____	Day _____
Time _____	Time _____	Time _____

THEME OF THE WEEK

Engage Your Core And Create Balance

Last week we started to work on our posture by paying attention to alignment and feeling the one-legged posture stance. Now we'll take it a step further by focusing on strengthening our core and relaxing our legs, arms, shoulders and anything else around that "Needle in Cotton." Only when you get aligned properly and engage your core can you then create the balance needed to be able to relax your arms and legs. The balance you create physically will help you learn the importance of balance in your life as a whole and lead to an all-encompassing balance that honors your vision and facilitates your journey forward in life.

Physical balance comes from first finding your center and then allowing everything around it to relax and move fluidly and freely. Practice the exercise on page 28 of the book or view Engage Your Core on the DVD. We want you to feel the difference between when you are engaging your core and when you are not. If you've never felt your core working, this is a great way to really feel it, as well as find it! Your core muscles stabilize your pelvis as you walk. Engaging them will help you to create balance in all your movement.

> *Your core is the home of your Chi, from which all your power emanates. Engaging your core and finding your inner balance go hand in hand. One cannot happen without the other.*

With the exception of the first walk of this week (the 20-minute test), this week's walks are relatively easy. You should do them all at a comfortable pace and not push any of your physical fitness limits. Remember: Form First. If you are used to walking longer distances, spend *at least* 20 minutes on your ChiWalking form at the start of every walk. If you're just getting started on a fitness program, do your best to complete at least 15-20 minutes of walking per session.

Core strength awareness and creating balance are the focal points this week. Practice leveling your pelvis and tiling your statue. Feel your upper body directly over your hips. Really feel your shoulders over your lead leg as it supports your weight. Feel your balance point moving forward with every step.

As you did prior to every walk last week, practice the One-legged Posture Stance before beginning each walk. Memorize how it feels when you're standing still so that you can achieve that same feeling while you're walking. Feel the difference between when your pelvis is level and when it's not. Move from one foot to the other, feeling the straight line from your head to your toe. Body Sense everything you're doing.

As you start walking, practice alternating between tilting and not tilting your statue. Get a sense of what happens when your shoulders are over your hips (tilting your statue) and when they are not. As you become aware of your balance during movement, feel your center of balance move forward as you tilt your statue. You might also notice that you walk a little faster with less effort!

Finding balance and engaging your core is so important that you should try to remember leveling your pelvis as often as you can throughout the week—no matter what you're doing or where you're walking. Whether you're standing in line at the supermarket, at the bank, or just standing in a group talking.

CHI-PRINCIPLE OF THE WEEK

Gradual Progress

This week, we're going to pay attention to the most basic of Chi-Principles: Gradual Progress. All things in life—from the growth of living creatures to the process of learning a new task, establishing a relationship with someone, or training for a competition—abide by this universal law. Few things in life, if any, emerge perfectly formed overnight. *(Read more on page 62 of the book.)*

Continue being mindful during your walks through focusing this week. Use your watch as a reminder during your one-minute intervals. You may feel a bit overwhelmed by the number of focuses to think about as you perfect your posture and master the ChiWalking technique. But relax. You don't have to learn them all at once. Take the time to learn each focus, one at a time, and you'll gradually build your reportoire. Remember: this is a gradual process that we're taking, one day and one step at a time. Part of the reason you use a watch with a beeper is so you can keep your mind focused on the lessons of the week. You are gathering strength and knowledge as you go along. Each day will become easier as you build upon the previous day's experience and then move ahead. Don't ever hesitate to look back and review any exercises and focuses. You can always return to an earlier lesson and repeat it.

Gradual Progress is a reminder to let ChiWalking and any new skills in your life develop slowly and consistently, all the while being patient with yourself.

WORKOUT #1

Today's Date: _____

LESSON: 5 MINUTES

• Watch the Posture Lesson on the DVD: Pay particular attention to the art of the leveling your pelvis while tilting your statue one-quarter inch forward.

RE-CAP The four key steps to proper alignment are:

1. **Align** your feet.

2. **Lengthen** your upper spine.

3. **Level** your pelvis.

4. **Tilt** your statue 1/4" forward from the hips.

When you have aligned your posture, check to ensure your shoulders are down and relaxed. Now close your eyes and feel your strong center core. Memorize what this feels like. A quick way to remember what to do is just think **A.L.L.T. - Align, Lengthen, Level, and Tilt.**

Walking Evaluation

Your first walk this week is a 20-minute Walking Test to evaluate your starting point. This will allow you to acknowledge and get aligned with where you're at today so you can measure your progress as you develop your own program and move closer to your goals. (This also helps you create, manage, and realize those goals.)

PRE-WALK BODY LOOSENERS: 5 Minutes

These exercises will relax your muscles and loosen your joints so that your walking will be more fluid. *(Refer to the "Body Looseners" section of the DVD or the book, pages 142-145.)* Remember, we're building upon a program already in motion, so you're going to first repeat last week's body looseners and then add a new one.

• Begin by shaking out your whole body like you're a rag doll. Be sure to shake your arms and legs thoroughly. Have fun with this. Really shake out your entire body. Feel your head, neck, shoulders, arms, hands, torso, abdomen, legs, and feet cut loose. Let it all go!

Then, do the following exercises:

• **Ankle rolls:** Do 10 clockwise circles and then 10 counter-clockwise circles. Switch legs and repeat the exercise.

• **Knee circles:** Do 10 clockwise circles and then 10 counter-clockwise circles.

• **Hip circles: Do 10 clockwise circles and then 10 counter-clockwise circles.**

Shake out that body again and **FEEL** your entire body from the top of your head all the way down to your toes.

Learn Post-Walk Stretches: *5 Minutes*
• Review how to do your post-walk stretches *now* so you can transition smoothly into stretching at the end of your walk. Refer to Appendix B in this workbook to review the calf stretch, achilles stretch, **hip flexor** and **hamstring stretch**.

Measure Your Heart Rate
You can use a heart rate monitor or for the low tech, low cost way do this:

Hold two fingers at the side of your neck next to your Adam's apple. Count your pulse for 15 seconds and multiply by 4 to get beats per minute.

MOVE FORWARD INTO YOUR WALK

20 Minute Walking Test

Today, you're simply going to walk and obtain a relative measurement of your health and physical fitness level. You'll check your heart rate after walking for 20 minutes. You'll take this assessment again in Week 6. This walk will provide a baseline for measuring your progress, which you'll record in the self assessment you'll be doing this week. The assessment you do this week will help you build upon your program and make plans according to your own personal needs and goals. We suggest that you repeat this assessment once a month so that you can watch your fitness level improve.

Here's how to do your 20-minute walking assessment:
(Refer to page 185-186 in the book.)

1. Walk on a flat surface – a track is the best.

2. Check your watch and walk for 20 minutes at a comfortably fast pace.

3. Upon finishing, do two things:

> 1. Take your pulse immediately (or look at your heart rate monitor).

> 2. Measure how far you have walked (or simply note a landmark and use the same starting point when you do you next assessment in a month).

When you do these assessments, you'll see if your heart rate is staying the same or decreasing (a sign of improved fitness), and you may find that in a few weeks you walk further with more ease.

POST WALK STRETCHES: 5 Minutes

Do your calf, achilles, **hip flexor**, and **hamstring** stretches.

✳ SEE YOU WHEN YOU GET BACK! ✳

END OF WALK REVIEW: 5 MINUTES

Congratulations on completing the 20-minute walk test. After your next session this week we'll have you record a detailed assessment on yourself, but right now just take note of the following questions.

Heart rate upon finishing: _____ beats per minute.

For how many minutes did you walk? _____

Could you keep the same quick pace for the duration of your walk? _____

On a scale of 1 to 10 (1 = awful/poor; 10 = excellent/great), how did you feel in the middle of your walk? _____

How about toward the end of your walk? _____

How did you feel immediately upon return? Did you have any aches or pains?

_____

_____

_____

_____

How do you feel now? Do you have any aches or pains?

_____

_____

_____

_____

Do you have anything else you'd like to record here? Go ahead and write down anything you want that we haven't already asked!

_____

_____

_____

_____

_____

FOCUSES IN BETWEEN SESSIONS

In gearing up for the next session, start focusing on keeping your **pelvis level** and finding that **inner balance**. Remember: You can do this just about anywhere, no matter what you're doing, cooking, cleaning, shopping, whatever. As you did last week, choose two times a day to set your mind on your **posture** and in particular, the balance you create when you engage your core, level your pelvis, and tilt your statue. (If you were successful with doing this twice a day last week, simply keep those times and do them again this week.)

Record here when those times are (even if they are the same as last week):

_____ and _____

RE-NEW YOUR COMMITMENT

I will do another ChiWalking session on this day:_____
(Write this date down on your calendar or in any daily planner you keep.)

One more thing before you go…Record Your Resting Heart Rate

In the morning, when you've just opened your eyes and discovered it's a new day, record your Resting Heart Rate (RHR) before you get out of bed (page 185 in the book). Jot down that important number right away. In combination with the results of your 20–minute walk and the assessment you'll complete in your next sessions, you'll have a good idea of your "starting point". At the end of this 8-week program your RHR may be lower, which means that your heart is getting stronger.

Write down your resting heart rate here:

_____beats per minute.

You'll be reminded to test your resting heart rate (RHR) in the first session every week, in the end of Walk Review. It is not necessary for everyone, but it is an indicator of your level of conditioning.

WORKOUT #2

Today's Date: _____

LESSON: 5 MINUTES

Review the Posture Lesson on the DVD (if you need to) with a focus on leveling your pelvis and tilting your statue. Really practice feeling the difference between tilting your statue and not. Memorize how it feels to level your pelvis and tilt your statue.

If possible, have someone push you backwards (gently of course) so you can feel how tilting your statue forward keeps you in balance.

> *Make a Choice to use your lower abdominal muscles to level your pelvis and engage your core. Most people lean backwards and tighten their glutes. Instead, focus on keeping a level pelvis, an engaged core, and relaxed glutes. Tilt your statue to move forward.*

PRE-WALK BODY LOOSENERS: 5 Minutes

(Refer to the DVD or pages 142-145 for more info.)

• Shake out your entire body from head to toe. Let it all out!
• Do your ankle rolls, knee circles, **hip circles**
Take a moment to **FEEL** every square inch of your body. Shake it out again if you like!

Review post-walk stretches: 5 minutes
(Refer to Appendix B to review the calf stretch, achilles stretch, **hip flexor, hamstring stretch**.)

MOVE FORWARD INTO YOUR WALK: 15-20 minutes

To reinforce your good posture, practice the One-legged Posture Stance before starting your walk with a focus on leveling your pelvis and tilting your statue.

Set your watch to beep every minute. Each beep becomes a cue to be mindful of your walk and your focuses. Overall, you're going to walk at a comfortable pace for 15-20 minutes.

FOCUSES DURING THE WALK

• First 5 minutes: **Tilt your statue.** Explore the feeling of balance by tilting your statue forward at varying distances. Notice how your speed increases the farther forward you lean. Play with this tilting motion and feel the difference between tilting a little bit and tilting a lot. Find your balancing point somewhere in between.

• Next 10 minutes: Do alternating 1-minute intervals of **leveling your pelvis**. Do, one minute on, one minute off.

• Last 5 minutes: Focus on tilting your statue and feeling the ground as you extend your head.

Be careful not to lean backward!
Many people lean backwards instead of forward,
which leads to all kinds of lower back, hip and knee problems!

POST WALK STRETCHES: 5 Minutes

Do your calf, achilles, **hip flexor**, **hamstring** stretches

✳ SEE YOU WHEN YOU GET BACK! ✳

WORKOUT #2   WEEK 2 - ENGAGE YOUR CORE!

END OF WALK REVIEW: 5 MINUTES

How many minutes did you walk? _____.

Describe how you feel right now? _____

_____

_____

_____

_____

Does tilting your statue help you feel your balance? _____

_____

Did you feel your speed pick up when you tilted your statue? _____

_____

Were you able to hold your pelvis level? _____

_____

Can you feel when you're tightening your glutes versus when you're using your lower
abdominals to level your pelvis? (It takes practice and persistence.) _____

_____

Is there anything you learned during today's walk? (Any realizations or understandings?)
What were they?

_____

_____

_____

_____

_____

_____

_____

PROGRAM DEVELOPMENT: 15 Minutes

Your Physical Assessment: Go to Appendix A: Week 2, Part 1

FOCUSES IN BETWEEN WORKOUTS

Pay attention to your form focuses between now and your next session. It only takes a minute to stop and get into your One-legged Posture Stance, and it takes only two seconds to practice:

- Getting aligned

- Leveling your pelvis

- Feeling your core

- Sensing your balance

Remember: You engage your core by leveling your pelvis, and you create balance by tilting your statue. Do this exercise as often as you can remember it, whenever you're walking anywhere, all week. Feel the subtlety of it. Don't engage too much, just use your lower abdominals. Practice isolating your lower abdominals without tightening your glutes! Gradual Progress is the goal. Be subtle yet effective.

RE-NEW YOUR COMMITMENT:

*I will start Workout #3 on this day:*_____
(Write this date down on your calendar or in any daily planner you keep.)

WORKOUT #3

Today's Date: _____

LESSON: 5 MINUTES

Review the **Posture Lesson** on the DVD (if you need to): Practice leveling your pelvis using your lower abdominal muscles…not your glutes. Pound your glutes if you need to, to feel them and teach them to relax!

Make a Choice to Tilt Your Statue
Once you've engaged your core and created balance by tilting your statue (really FEEL that balance), tilt your statue on and off—tilt more, tilt less. FEEL your center and the balance created by it.

> *If possible, have someone push you backwards (gently of course) so you can feel how tilting your statue forward keeps you in balance.*

PRE-WALK BODY LOOSENERS: 5 Minutes

(Refer to the DVD or pages 142-145 in the book for more info.)

• Shake out your entire body from head to toe. Let loose!
• Do your ankle rolls, knee circles, hip circles

> *Take a moment to FEEL every square inch of your body.*
> *Inhale a big, deep breath that fills your lungs from the bottom up and pushes out your belly.*
> *Then exhale completely, relaxing your chest first.*

Review post-walk stretches: *5 minutes*
(Refer to Appendix B to review the calf stretch, achilles stretch, **hip flexor, hamstring stretch** if necessary.)

MOVE FORWARD INTO YOUR WALK: 20 minutes

Dedicate at least 20 minutes to your walk today. Set your watch timer for one-minute intervals. Walk at a comfortable pace for 20 minutes and practice leveling your pelvis while tilting your statue.

FOCUSES DURING THE WALK

• First 5 minutes: **Tilt your statue.** Explore the feeling of balance by tilting your statue forward at varying degrees. Notice how your speed increases the farther forward you lean. Play with this tilting motion and feel the difference between tilting a little bit and tilting a lot. Find the balancing point that allows you to move forward without straining your back or over-working your legs.

• Next 10 minutes: Do 1-minute intervals of **leveling your pelvis**. Do one minute on, one minute off.

• Last 5 minutes: Focus on that **one-legged posture stance** (yet again!) from the ground up to your extending head. Repeat these exercises regularly and you'll always move toward health and vitality.

Be careful not to lean backwards!
Many people lean backwards instead of forwards,
which leads to all kinds of problems!

POST WALK STRETCHES: 5 Minutes

Do your calf, achilles, hip flexor, hamstring stretches.

✳ SEE YOU WHEN YOU GET BACK! ✳

END OF WALK REVIEW: 5 MINUTES

How many minutes did you walk? _____

Describe how you feel right now? _____

_____

_____

_____

Do you have any aches or pains? If so, what? _____

_____

How well were you able to keep your posture aligned while walking? _____

Were you able to hold your pelvis level? _____

Were there any posture focuses you had trouble doing or remembering?

_____

_____

Could you sense in your body when it was time to stop walking?

_____

_____

How did you feel as soon as you stopped walking?

_____

_____

Is there anything you learned during today's walk? (Any realizations or understandings?)
What were they?

_____

_____

_____

_____

PROGRAM DEVELOPMENT: 15 Minutes

Assess Your Attitude: Go to Appendix A, Program Development, Week 2, Part 2

Congratulations on finishing Week 2. You have a reason to smile. You are building the foundation for healthy movement by creating alignment, a stronger core, and creating balance with every step you take. If you plan to do more walking this week, continue to practice all the posture exercises. Most importantly, relax and have fun with the process!

Remember to
STOP AND PRACTICE YOUR POSTURE AT LEAST TWICE A DAY
between now and next week!

RE-NEW YOUR COMMITMENT:

I will start Weekt #3 on this day:_____.
(Write this date down on your calendar or in any daily planner you keep.)

WEEK 3 OVERVIEW

Theme of the Week: Upper Body Forward and Legs out the Back

Chi-Skill: Body Sensing
- Listening to your Body
- The Body Scan

Minimum Time Commitment: 3 x 1-hour workouts, 3 hours total

Body Looseners: Ankles - knees - hips - **sacrum - and pelvic rotations**

3 Walks: Comfortable pace, smooth and flat terrain
1. 25-30 min. walk developing a consistent stride length, practicing the body scan
2. 25-30 min. walk practicing "tilt the statue" and swinging legs to the rear
3. 25-30 min. walk fast and slow intervals with various focuses

Post Walk Stretches:
calf stretch, achilles stretch, hip flexor stretch, hamstring stretch, **adductor stretch**

Program Development: Establishing Goals

What to re-read in the book: Chapter 2, page 32; Chapter 3, pages 43-48; Chapter 4, pages 84-90; Chapter 6, pages 170 ("Body Scan"); and Chapter 7, pages 187-191.

What to review on DVD: Lesson Two: Lower Body Focuses plus the Body Scan exercise. (Watch the DVD on the first workout of this week, then, if necessary, at the start of your second and third workouts for reinforcement.)

Write in the days and times for your 3 sessions this week:

Workout #1	Workout #2	Workout #3
Day _____	Day _____	Day _____
Time _____	Time _____	Time _____

Let Your Upper Body Lead – Legs Out the Back

Now that you have a feel for good posture, you'll be using your column as the basis for all your forward movement. This week you'll practice moving forward leading with your upper body while your legs swing out the back. This may be the biggest shift you'll make in learning ChiWalking. The sensation is quite different from leading with your legs, as most people do. Here is where it is crucial for you to Make a Choice to walk in a new way. Leading with your upper body engages your core, which will give you long term strength and endurance with your walking. It will also save your knees and hips from pain and overuse.

The first step is to find your ideal stride length, which we'll do in our first lesson. Your stride length will be much shorter than you're used to. This also will feel funny, but you'll soon feel the energy that comes from walking with a shorter stride length. You won't be overworking your legs and your lower back and it creates less impact on your joints. Try it! Soon you'll appreciate the benefits, even if it feels odd at first.

Remember: Lead with your upper body by tilting your statue and let your legs swing out behind you. This balanced and stable way to walk will give you more power and endurance.

In the first workout this week you will practice the Slow Motion Walk. Really feel your leg straightening out the back. Keep your stride short and consistent. When you tilt your statue, you'll feel your lower abdominal muscles working more than normal, and you will also notice how it helps you move forward with greater ease. That's because as you tilt your statue, you're letting gravity pull you forward. Stay with your posture and these new practices and your walking will become smoother and easier. Whenever you feel tired, just shorten your stride and tilt your statue… and you'll give your legs a much needed rest.

Feel your upper body directly over your hips while walking. Find and play with your balance point. Tilt your statue, then don't, then tilt your statue again. Find the "Sweet Spot" that's just right for you.

Your walks this week will be a little longer; plan to devote between 25 and 30 minutes to each walking portion. If you feel like you're not ready to walk that much yet, that's okay. Just listen to your body and don't push yourself beyond what you're capable of doing. This may be one of the more challenging weeks as you learn new movements and add to your repertoire of focuses. Keep at it and it will pay off!

CHI-SKILL OF THE WEEK

Body Sensing

(Read pages 43-48 of the book and Body Scan in the DVD.)
Your body is always talking to you and you can learn a lot by listening to what it has to say. Here we're going to practice "listening." In your workouts this week we'll ask you to take time to do regular Body Scans. Practice doing a Body Scan at various junctures throughout your day, whether you're walking, sitting, or lying down. The Body Scan is a great way to tune your mind into your body and ask, "What's going on?" Go point to point from your head to toes and ask yourself, "Is there any tension here? Is this really relaxed? Tight? Sore? Can I make this feel better?"

Taking a time-out to scan your body and pay close attention to any tense areas is one of the most important features of Body Sensing. By Body Sensing, you make your body a number one priority and get in tune with how it feels. Through Body Sensing, you can build that strong connection between your mind and body, which is a key goal of ChiWalking.

> *Doing a Body Scan will reinforce all those magical connections between your mind and body.*
> *For a quick way to "locate" yourself in your body, feel your butt on your seat while sitting, or even better, feel your feet touching the ground.*

WORKOUT #1

Today's Date: _____

LESSON: 15 MINUTES

• Watch Lesson 2, Part 1: Determine Your Ideal Stride Length
• Follow along with the DVD to determine your ideal stride length; notice how short it is!
• Watch Additional Exercises: The Body Scan
• Do your first body scan as you listen to the instructions of this important body sensing technique on the DVD

PRE-WALK BODY LOOSENERS: 5 Minutes

Use either the DVD to review your body looseners and learn the new ones for this week, or refer to the book (pages 142-148). Remember to repeat the same looseners as last week and add the **Sacrum Circles** and **Pelvic Rotations** to the menu this week.

• Begin by shaking out your whole body like you're a rag doll. Be sure to shake your arms and legs thoroughly. Have fun with this…really shake out your entire body.

Then, do the following exercises:
• **Ankle rolls:** Do 10 clockwise circles and then 10 counter-clockwise.
Switch legs and repeat the exercise.
• **Knee Circles:** Do 10 clockwise circles and then 10 counter-clockwise circles.
• **Hip Circles:** Do 10 clockwise circles and then 10 counter-clockwise circles.
• **Sacrum Circles:** Do 10 clockwise circles and then 10 counter-clockwise circles.
• **Pelvic Rotations:** Do a few rotations on each leg.

Shake out that body again. Begin to FEEL your physical being from the top of your head all the way down to your toes.

Learn Post-Walk Stretches: 5 Minutes
• Review how to do your post-walk stretches now so you can transition into doing your stretches upon return. Refer to Appendix B to review the calf stretch, achilles stretch, hip flexor stretch, hamstring stretch, and **adductor stretch**.

MOVE FORWARD INTO YOUR WALK: 25-30 minutes

Set your watch so it beeps every minute. Really use those one-minute reminders to stay mindful in your practice. Here's the breakdown for this walk:

FOCUSES DURING THE WALK

• First 2 minutes: Using a very short stride, do the **Slow Motion Walk** for 30 seconds, then walk at a comfortable pace. Repeat the sequence, walking in slow motion, then picking up the pace. Notice how your cadence changes but not the length of your stride as you go between a slow motion walk and a regular paced walk.

• Next 15 minutes: Resume an easy, comfortable pace, but intentionally **keep your stride length shorter** than you're used to until the end of your walk. Don't force yourself to take smaller strides, relax and it will happen. Feel your **statue tilting slightly forward** while your **legs sweep out the back** in short strides. Feel your center of gravity and your **balance forward**.

• Last 10-15 minutes: Practice doing the **Body Scan**, starting with your feet and working your way up your body to your head. Move slowly and take time to really sense each area of your body. Watch for any muscle tension or tightness in your joints. When you're finished with your walk, write down any areas you felt stiff or tight, so you can work at releasing tension in those areas at all times.

Feel your shoulders directly over your support leg with each forward step. Remember to lean forward, not back!

POST WALK STRETCHES: 5 Minutes

Do your calf, achilles, hip flexor, hamstring, and adductor stretches.

✳ SEE YOU WHEN YOU GET BACK! ✳

END OF WALK REVIEW: 5 MINUTES

How many minutes did you walk? _____

How did you feel immediately upon return? From your Body Scan did you feel any areas that were tense or tight? (Between now and your next walk, see if you can feel that tension and practice relaxing that area of your body.)

_____

_____

_____

_____

How did the shorter stride feel? _____

_____

_____

Were you able to keep your "statue" tilted while walking?_____

Could you sense that your shoulders were over your feet with each step? How did it feel when you were able to?

_____

_____

Is there anything you learned during today's walk? (Any realizations or understandings? What were they?

_____

_____

_____

_____

_____

Optional notes (for the first workout for the week):
Resting heart rate (RHR): _____beats per minute.

It is best to do it first thing in the morning.

FOCUSES IN BETWEEN WORKOUTS

Twice a day last week you focused on your posture and, in particular, the balance you create when you engage your core, level your pelvis, and tilt your statue. Repeat this focus at least twice a day this week. Really focus on your tilt. Play with your balance and try to Body Sense the perfect amount of tilt.

Do Body Scans regularly. Tune into what your body is saying to you or asking of you. Is it tense or tight in some areas? Try to relax it. If you learn to listen intently to your body, you'd be surprised by what you might hear! Identify what your body needs and nourish it from the inside out. You have the power to intervene, make positive choices today, and see real results tomorrow.

RE-NEW YOUR COMMITMENT

I will do another ChiWalking session on this day:_____.
(Write this date down on your calendar or in any daily planner you keep.)

WORKOUT #2

Today's Date: _____

LESSON: 5 MINUTES

- Watch Lesson 2, Part 2: Upper body Forward – Legs Out the Back
- Practice the Slow Motion Walk along with the DVD
- Review the Body Scan exercise on the DVD (if you need to)

> *Body Scan Time. Before doing your pre-walk looseners today, take a minute or two to practice body sensing by conducting a Body Scan. Pretend your mind is an MRI machine. Start at your feet and end at the top of your head, scanning every nook and cranny of yourself. Anything tight? Sore? Tingly? Be mindful of every sensation moving through you right now. Identify any tense areas.*
> *Focus on loosening them up on your walk.*

PRE-WALK BODY LOOSENERS: 5 Minutes

(Refer to the DVD or pages 142-148 of the book for more info.)

- Shake out your entire body from head to toe.
- Then do your ankle rolls, knee circles, hip circles, sacrum circles, and pelvic rotations.
Take a moment to FEEL every square inch of your body. Shake it out again if you like!

Review post-walk stretches: 2 minutes
(Refer to Appendix B to review the calf stretch, achilles stretch, hip flexor, hamstring stretch, and adductor stretch, if necessary.)

MAKE A CHOICE:

Before commencing your walk today, have the intention to walk with a shorter stride and with your upper body leading.

MOVE FORWARD INTO YOUR WALK   25-30 minutes

Now you're ready to get walking. This walk's theme will be **tilting your statue slightly forward** while allowing your **legs** to **extend out the back** with each stride.

FOCUSES DURING THE WALK

• First 2 minutes: Practice your **shortened stride** while walking at a slow pace. Mentally go through all the posture focuses and feel how straight your **posture** is. Once you can consistently feel your **one-legged posture stance** with each footstep, change to a comfortable pace.

• Next 25 minutes: One minute intervals alternating between **tilting your statue** and **leveling your pelvis**. Be aware of tilting your statue to the point where you always feel like your **shoulders are directly over your hips** with each stride. As you begin to feel your statue tilting forward relax your legs and let them sweep out the back in short strides. Feel your **pelvis level** and your **center of gravity forward**.

• Last 3 minutes: For the last 3 minutes of your walk, relax your entire body.

Feel your shoulders directly over your support leg with each forward step.
Remember to lean forward, not back.
Let gravity do the work—not your legs!

POST WALK STRETCHES: 5 Minutes

Do your calf, achilles, hip flexor, hamstring, and adductor stretches

✳ **SEE YOU WHEN YOU GET BACK!** ✳

END OF WALK REVIEW: 5 MINUTES

How many minutes did you walk? _____

How did you feel at the end of your walk?

_____
_____
_____
_____

How did a shorter stride feel?

_____
_____

Were you able to keep your "statue" tilted forward while walking?

_____
_____

Could you sense that your shoulders were over your feet with each step?

_____
_____

Could you feel the difference in your stride when they were?

_____
_____
_____

Is there anything you learned during today's walk? (Any realizations or understandings?)
What were they?

_____
_____
_____
_____

PROGRAM DEVELOPMENT: 15 Minutes

Physical and Emotional Goals:
Go to Appendix A: Program Development Week 3, Part 1

FOCUSES IN BETWEEN WORKOUTS

Keep taking time-out in your day to **practice your alignment** and really get in tune with how it feels in your body. (Tip: Tilt up the rear-view mirror in your car so you have to **sit up straighter** to see out the back. It works great!) Use body sensing as a way to really enjoy the sensations of your body. Feel the rhythm of your breath. That tingling in your body means your alive—that's Chi and the more you appreciate it, the more it will grow.

RE-NEW YOUR COMMITMENT:

I will start Workout #3 on this day:_____
(Write this date down on your calendar or in any daily planner you keep.)

Workout #3

Today's Date: _____

Review: 5 Minutes (optional if you want)
- Lesson 2 Part 1 and 2, and the Body Scan exercise on the DVD (if you need to)
- Body Looseners for the week
- Post-walk stretches for the week

Body Scan Time. As in your second workout this week, take a minute or two to practice Body Sensing by doing a full body sweep prior to doing your looseners. Scan your body from head to toe. Anything tight? Sore? Tingly? Be mindful of every sensation moving through you right now. Do your body looseners before walking and if you find any tight spots, continue to work on relaxing them during your walk.

PRE-WALK BODY LOOSENERS: 5 Minutes

- Shake out your entire body from head to toe. Get loose!
- Then, do your ankle rolls, knee circles, hip circles, sacrum circles, and pelvic rotations.

Take a moment to FEEL every square inch of your body.
Inhale a big, deep breath that fills your lungs from the bottom up and pushes out your belly.
Then exhale completely, relaxing your chest first.
FEEL your body once more. Shake it again if you like!

FOCUSES DURING THE WALK

• First 2 minutes: Warm up at an easy pace and think about any focuses that you feel you'd like to keep in mind today. Also work on the theme of the week. **Tilting your upper body forward** while letting your **legs swing to the rear**. Didn't we tell you that this is a course in multi-tasking?

• Next 25 minutes: After warming up, resume a comfortable pace. Set your countdown timer and do one-minute intervals at fast and slow paces. One minute fast, one minute slow. One minute fast, one minute slow, fast, slow, fast, slow, and so on. Whether you're moving at a fast or slow pace, concentrate on the following for one minute each.

1st minute: keep your pelvis level and tilt your statue

2nd minute: maintain short, equal strides out the back with the rear leg
             straightening as it swings.

MAKE A CHOICE:

If you haven't yet walked a full 30 minutes this week, make an intention to do so today. The only way to walk farther is to choose to do it and then stick with your decision.

Before starting your walk today, spend a couple of minutes practicing your posture and finding your stride. Refer back to Workout 2 for a re-cap, or use the DVD.

POST WALK STRETCHES: 5 Minutes

Do your calf, achilles, hip flexor, hamstring, and adductor stretches.

✳ SEE YOU WHEN YOU GET BACK! ✳

END OF WALK REVIEW: 5 MINUTES

How many minutes did you walk? _____

How did you feel at the end of your walk?_____
_____
_____
_____

How do you feel now?_____
_____
_____
_____

How did the shorter stride feel?_____
_____

Were you able to keep your "statue" tilted slightly forward?
_____

Did you hold your shoulders over your hips with each step? _____

Could you feel the difference in your stride when you did?_____
_____
_____

Did you learn anything new about yourself during today's walk? (Any realizations or under-standings?)
_____
_____
_____
_____
_____
_____

PROGRAM DEVELOPMENT: 10 Minutes

Mental and Metaphysical Goals:
Got to Appendix A: Program Development, Week 3, Part 2

Congratulations on finishing Week 3! You've already come a long way since beginning this journey just a few weeks ago. Take a deep belly breath. Do a quick body scan once more before closing out today's workout. Absorb how you feel inside and out, from your mind to your muscles. As you finish this week, notice the effect ChiWalking has on your everyday life, such as when you're shopping, moving away from your car, or walking around your office. You'll be amazed by how great you feel when you're aligned, balanced, and "fully engaged."

Keep in mind this question throughout your day: Are you letting your upper body tilt forward so gravity can pull you forward and do most of the work?

RE-NEW YOUR COMMITMENT

I will start Week 4 on this day:_____
(Write this date down on your calendar or in any daily planner you keep.)

WEEK 4 OVERVIEW

Theme of the Week: Lower Body Fluidity

Chi-Principle: Needle in Cotton

Minimum Time Commitment: *4 x 60-70 minute workouts, 4 hours total*

Body Looseners: ankles knees hips, sacrum, and pelvic rotations, **spine rolls**, and **spinal twist**.

4 Walks: Smooth and flat terrain
1. 25-30 minute walk with focuses
2. 25-30 minute walk with focuses
3. 25-30 minute walk with focuses
4. 20-25 minute walk: The Calming Walk

Post Walk Stretches:
calf stretch, achilles stretch, hip flexor stretch, hamstring stretch, adductor stretch, **quadriceps stretch**

Program Development: Create a balanced program

What to re-read in the book: Chapter 2, page 23-24; Chapter 3, pages 48-50;

Chapter 4, pages 85-89; and Chapter 5, pages 129-130 (The Calming Walk).

What to re-view on DVD: Lesson Two: Lower Body Focuses plus the Body Scan exercise. Watch the DVD on the first workout of this week, then, if necessary, at the start of your second and third workout for reinforcement.

Program Development: Establishing Goals

Write in the days and times for your 4 sessions this week:

Workout #1	Workout #2	Workout #3	Workout #4
Day _____	Day _____	Day _____	Day _____
Time _____	Time _____	Time _____	Time _____

THEME OF THE WEEK

Needle in Cotton:
Gather to Your Center and Let Go of All Else

Needle in Cotton is one of the fundamental principles in ChiWalking and we're going to help you reinforce it in your body this week. Hold the image of a needle running through the center of a ball of cotton—the needle represents a thin straight line running vertically through the rotational axis of your body, along your spine. Gather energy (chi) to this centerline and initiate all movement from it. The more energy you gather toward your center—your needle—the more you must let go of holding energy elsewhere. You shoulders and arms, hips and legs are as loose and soft as cotton.

> *Call to mind the motion of a top-loading washing machine*
> *for a visual image.*
> *The clothes (the cotton) move fluidly around the spindle (the spine),*
> *and there's no resistance (no tension).*

To apply this important principle to your body and create that Needle in Cotton, start by getting aligned, and then pick up your heels and relax your lower legs. Overworking your lower legs can cause injuries and is a waste of good energy. When you push your body forward, you employ all those small lower leg muscles—your calves and shins—which are not built for that kind of work. How do you save your lower leg muscles from unnecessary and sometimes painful work? Stop using them. That's right: Learn to RELAX your lower legs by using the forward tilt of your upper body and the rotation of your pelvis to drive your legs and move you forward. Your abs and core muscles will get a great workout and your legs will do what they're supposed to do: support your body weight. If you let them stick to what they are good at, you can then keep your energy centered and your movement fluid.

Another part of maintaining that Needle in Cotton is allowing your spine to twist and your pelvis to rotate. Now we come to the good part. This lesson is about moving from your center and putting your core muscles, pelvis and hips to good use. Here you'll learn to rotate your pelvis around your central axis (Needle in Cotton). Because your core muscles are engaged by leveling your pelvis, your pelvis will remain stable, yet it will rotate around your central axis providing a powerful driving force for your legs. *This* is the engine that will: 1) move you forward, 2) ensure that your core gets stronger with every step and, 3) keep you from overworking your legs. Also, when you learn to rotate your pelvis from your pivot point, it works wonders for relaxing your lower back.

> *Body Sense being able to rotate your pelvis while holding it level at the same time. Practice this as often as you can!*

You'll do four walks this week, the last one is from the ChiWalking menu. Make a Choice to complete all four walks, even if you can't do all of them for as long as suggested. Your last walk can be shorter than the first three workouts, since it is a new add-on. Continue to listen to your body by doing body scans throughout the day.

Workout #1

Today's Date: _____

• Review Lesson 2 on the DVD: 15 Minutes
• Watch Lesson 2, Part 3: Pick Up Your Heels and Relax Your Lower Legs
• Follow along with the DVD and do the standing and walking heel lift exercises

PRE-WALK BODY LOOSENERS: 5 Minutes

Use either the DVD to review your body looseners and learn the new ones for this week, or refer to the book (pages 142-151).

• Begin by shaking out your whole body like you're a rag doll. Be sure to shake your arms and legs thoroughly. Have fun with this. Really shake out your entire body: your head, neck, shoulders, arms, hands, torso, legs, and feet. Let it all go!

Then, do the following exercises:

• Ankle rolls: Do 10 clockwise circles and then 10 counter-clockwise circles. Switch legs and repeat the exercise.
• Knee Circles: Do 10 clockwise circles and then 10 counter-clockwise circles.
• Hip Circles: Do 10 clockwise circles and then 10 counter-clockwise circles.
• Sacrum Circles: Do 10 clockwise circles and then 10 counter-clockwise circles.
• Pelvic Rotations: Do a few rotations on each leg.
• **Spine Rolls:** Do 3 repeats.
• **Spinal Twist:** Do 3 repeats.

Shake out your body again.
FEEL your physical being from the top of your head
all the way down to your toes.

Learn Post-Walk Stretches: 5 Minutes
Review how to do your post-walk stretches now so you can transition correctly out of your walk upon return. Refer to Appendix B to review the calf Stretch, achilles stretch, hip flexor stretch, hamstring stretch, adductor stretch, and quadriceps stretch.

MOVE FORWARD INTO YOUR WALK:　　25-30 MINUTES

Set your watch to beep every minute. Use these one-minute reminders to staying mindful during your practice. Here's the breakdown for this walk:

FOCUSES DURING THE WALK

• First 5 minutes: Warm up at a strolling pace. Practice **relaxing your lower legs** with each stride. **Peel each foot off the ground** as you pick up your heels and lift them forward. As each heel leaves the ground, your ankles should be so relaxed that your toes drop down.

• Next 15-20 minutes: Pick up your pace a bit and continuing to do what you've been do-ing. Also, work on any previous focuses you feel a need to practice from previous lessons.* Stay relaxed and try to remember your heel lift as often as possible, no matter which other focuses you might be working on. This is mindful walking at its best.

*Choose two focuses from the previous weeks that are most challenging for you and incorporate them into your walk.

Focus #1 _____

Focus #2 _____

• Last 5 minutes: Cool down at a strolling pace.

> *Remember the Five Mindful Steps:*
> *1) Get Aligned, 2) Engage Your Core, 3) Create Balance,*
> *4) Make a Choice, and 5) Move Forward!*

POST WALK STRETCHES: 5 Minutes

Do your calf, achilles, hip flexor, hamstring, adductor, and quadriceps stretches.

✳ SEE YOU WHEN YOU GET BACK! ✳

END OF WALK REVIEW: 5 MINUTES

Welcome back. Let's take a few quick notes.

How many minutes did you walk? _____.

Could you feel the difference between picking up your heels and pushing off with your toes?

_____

With each stride, could you feel your legs straightening behind you at a comfortable stride length?

_____

_____

Could you relax your toes, ankles, and calves as you moved forward?

_____

_____

Were you able to let your toes drop as you walked?_____

_____

Could you imagine that Needle in Cotton…or possibly feel it?_____

_____

Which other focuses from previous walks did you bring in?

_____

_____

_____

_____

_____

_____

Optional (for first workout of week):
Resting Heart Rate (RHR) _____beats per minute.

Any other focuses in particular you think you should work on in future walks?

_____

_____

_____

_____

_____

Is there anything you learned about yourself during today's walk? (Any realizations or understandings?) What were they?

_____

_____

_____

_____

_____

_____

_____

_____

_____

PROGRAM DEVELOPMENT: 10 Minutes

Create a Balanced Program
Go to Appendix A: Program Development, Week 4, Part 1

FOCUSES IN BETWEEN WORKOUTS

Keep working on your posture. Also, check in once in a while with yourself by doing a quick Body Scan. Whenever you're walking this week, relax your lower legs. Pick up your heels, and let your toes drop downward. If you feel tension in your calves, ankles, or toes… stop and do your heel lift exercises. Imagine that you're p-e-e-l-i-n-g your foot off the ground as if it were a postage stamp you're peeling off a roll.

RE-NEW YOUR COMMITMENT

I will do another ChiWalking session on this day:_____
(Write this date down on your calendar or in any daily planner you keep.)

Workout #2

Today's Date: _____

LESSON: 5 MINUTES

• Review Lesson 2 on the DVD (if necessary)
• Watch Lesson 2, Part 4: Allow Your Spine to Twist and Your Pelvis to Rotate
• Practice the pelvic rotation exercise along with the DVD

> *Time-out for a Body Scan! Before doing your pre-walk looseners today, take a minute or two to practice body sensing by conducting a full body sweep. Start at your feet and end at the top of your head. Anything tight? Sore? Tingly? Be mindful of every sensation moving through you as you move into doing your Body Looseners.*

PRE-WALK BODY LOOSENERS: 5 Minutes

(Refer to the DVD or pages 142-151 of the book.)

• Shake out your entire body from head to toe.
• Then do your ankle rolls, knee circles, hip circles, sacrum circles, pelvic rotations, spine rolls, and spinal twists.

Take a moment to FEEL every square inch of your body. Shake it out again if you like!

Review Post-Walk Stretches: 5 Minutes
(Refer to Appendix B to review the calf stretch, achilles stretch, hip flexor, hamstring stretch, adductor stretch, and quadriceps stretch, if necessary.)

TIME TO GET WALKING!

Set your countdown timer for one-minute intervals. When you hear the beeper, check in on your posture, and remember your focuses.

FOCUSES DURING THE WALK

• First 5 minutes: Warm up at a strolling pace. Practice **relaxing your lower legs** with each stride. **Peel each foot off the ground** as you **pick up your heel** to lift it forward. As your heel leaves the ground, your ankles should be so relaxed that your toes drop down.
• Next 20-25 minutes: Walk at a medium pace and focus on alternating one-minute intervals of: a) **straightening your legs behind you** with each stride, and b) feeling your entire **lower body rotating below your pivot point**.

Remember: The center of your twist is at T-12/L-1, which is the medical term for where your twelfth (lowest) thoracic vertebra meets your first lumbar vertebra.
In traditional Chinese medicine,
this is one of the main points where Chi enters the body!

POST WALK STRETCHES: 5 Minutes

Do your calf, achilles, hip flexor, hamstring, and adductor, and **quadriceps** stretches.

✱ SEE YOU WHEN YOU GET BACK! ✱

END OF WALK REVIEW: 5 MINUTES

How many minutes did you walk?_____

Did you feel the difference between picking up your heels and pushing off with your toes?
_____

With each stride, could you feel your legs straightening behind you at a comfortable stride length?_____

Could you feel your toes, ankles, and calves relax as you moved forward? _____
_____

Did your toes drop down as you picked up your heels? _____
_____

How well could you sense the location of your pivot point at T12/L1? _____
_____
_____

Could you feel your spine twist at your pivot point as you walked?
_____
_____

Could you feel everything below your pivot-point moving as a sinlge fluid unit?
_____
_____
_____

Is there anything you learned during today's walk? (Any realizations or understandings?)
_____
_____
_____
_____
_____

FOCUSES IN BETWEEN WORKOUTS

Continue to check in on your posture. Relax your lower legs while walking and feel the twist at your pivot point. Also, Body Sense as much as you can.

RE-NEW YOUR COMMITMENT

I will do another ChiWalking session on this day:_____
(Write this date down on your calendar or in any daily planner you keep.)

Workout #3
Today's Date: _____

REVIEW: 5 MINUTES

• Lesson 2 on the DVD (if you need to)

PRE-WALK BODY LOOSENERS: 5 Minutes

(Refer to pages 142-151 of the book or the DVD.)

• Shake out your entire body from head to toe. Get loose!
• Take a minute to Body Scan slowly, feet to head.
• Do your ankle rolls, knee circles, hip circles, sacrum circles, and pelvic rotations, spine rolls, and spinal twists.

Take a moment to FEEL every square inch of your body.
Inhale a big, deep breath that fills your lungs from the bottom up
and pushes out your belly.
Then exhale completely, relaxing your chest first.
FEEL your body once more. Shake it again if you like!

Review Post-Walk Stretches: 5 Minutes (if necessary)
(Refer to Appendix B to review the calf stretch, achilles stretch, hip flexor, hamstring stretch, adductor stretch, and quadriceps stretch.)

MOVE FORWARD INTO YOUR WALK: 30 MINUTES

Set the countdown timer on your watch for one-minute intervals.

FOCUSES DURING THE WALK

• First 5 minutes: Begin walking at an easy pace. Keep your stride length short and try to **feel your pivot point twisting** with each stride. Then try to **level your pelvis** at the same time. You might not be able to hold your pelvis level for very long at first. But, the more you practice holding your pelvis level, the stronger your lower abdominal muscles will get.

> *Rotating your lower body from your pivot point allows you to level your pelvis and rotate it at the same time.*

• Next 20 minutes: Increase your speed up to a medium pace. Pay attention to your count-down timer and do the following three focuses, alternating them at one-minute intervals. (In the span of 20 minutes, you'll do each focus 7 times!)
> 1. Level your pelvis
> 2. Tilt your statue
> 3. Rotate your pelvis from your pivot point

• Last 5 minutes: Hold all three focuses at the same time.

> *Feel your statue tilting while your legs sweep out the back in comfortable, short strides. Peel your heels off the ground and relax your lower legs. You should feel no burning sensation on the back of your heels.*

POST WALK STRETCHES: 5 Minutes

Do your calf, achilles, hip flexor, hamstring, and adductor, and quadriceps stretches.

✳ SEE YOU WHEN YOU GET BACK! ✳

END OF WALK REVIEW: 5 MINUTES

How many minutes did you walk? _____

Were you able to hold your pelvis level for the entirety of each one minute interval?

_____

As you leveled your pelvis, did you find it easier to tilt your statue?

_____

How well could you sense the location of your pivot point?

_____

Did you find it easier to rotate your pelvis when you concentrated on your pivot point?

_____

Could you feel everything below your pivot point moving as one fluid unit?

_____

_____

Could you hold all three focuses at the end of your walk?

_____

_____

Which focus, if any, was difficult to hold?

_____

_____

Is there anything you learned during today's walk? (Any realizations or understandings?)
What were they?

_____

_____

_____

_____

_____

Workout #4

Today's Date: _____

PRE-WALK BODY LOOSENERS: 5 Minutes

(Refer to the DVD or pages 142-151 of the book.)

• Shake out your entire body from head to toe. Let loose!
• Take a minute to Body Scan. Watch for any tight areas. Loosen up before you loosen up!
• Then do your ankle rolls, knee circles, hip circles, sacrum circles, and pelvic rotations, spine rolls, and spinal twists.

Body Looseners are the best transition into a walk, and out of your busy life. It's time to focus on you!

MOVE FORWARD INTO YOUR WALK: 20-35 MINUTES

Calming Walk

This is your fourth walk this week (YES!!!!). Today we'll introduce you to The Calming Walk from the ChiWalking Matrix in Appendix C, pg. 194 of this workbook or in the book on page 137. The book suggests that you spend 30-45 minutes on this walk. But, since this is your fourth walk this week feel free to make it any length beyond 20 minutes, as long as it feels comfortable. (See pages 129-132 in the book.) The Calming Walk is about doing whatever it takes to settle your energy. Use the focuses below to help.

FOCUSES DURING THE WALK

• First 5 minutes: Begin walking at a slow and relaxing pace, keeping your stride comfortable and short. If you can, breathe only through your nose. On each in-breath, feel your **chest expand with calming energy**. Then, on your out-breath, **direct that energy down your spine**, like a waterfall.

• Next 10-15 minutes: Continue to walk slowly, while breathing in and out through your nose.

• Last 5 minutes: Cool down at a strolling pace without doing the focuses.

POST WALK STRETCHES: 5 Minutes

Do your calf, achilles, hip flexor, hamstring, and adductor, and quadriceps stretches.

✻ SEE YOU WHEN YOU GET BACK! ✻

END OF WALK REVIEW: 5 MINUTES

How many minutes did you walk? _____.

How well did you think you maintained your posture as you did your Calming Walk?

_____

_____

_____

_____

How did you feel afterwards?

_____

_____

_____

_____

Did you sense the energy from your head moving downward with every breath?

_____

_____

Were you able to breathe only through your nose? (If you couldn't, don't worry. What's important is that you direct your energy downward with each breath.)

_____

_____

Is there anything you learned during today's walk? (Any realizations or understandings?) What were they?

_____

_____

_____

_____

_____

Congratulations on finishing Week 4! Take a moment to reflect on the past four weeks and give yourself a pat on the back for being halfway through this workbook.

Now get your calendar out and start planning walks for Week 5!

FOCUSES IN BETWEEN WORKOUTS

Between now and your next workout, take time-out to focus on posture. Whenever you're walking, relax your lower legs and feel your spine twist at your pivot point.

Remember the Needle in Cotton! Get aligned, gather to your center, and let everything else relax…

RE-NEW YOUR COMMITMENT

I will start ChiWalking WEEK 5 on this day:_____
(Write this date down on your calendar or in any daily planner you keep.)

WEEK 5 OVERVIEW

Theme of the Week: Upper Body Focuses, Cadence & Arm Swing

Chi-Skill: Flexibility

Minimum Time Commitment: 4 x 1 hour workouts, 4 hours total

Body Looseners: ankles, knees hips, sacrum, pelvic rotations, **spine & grounding stance**

4 Walks: Smooth and flat terrain

1. One 25-30 min. walk using metronome in 3 different cadences, being aware of the T12/L1 pivot point
2. One 25-30 min. walk using metronome in different cadences, choosing two focuses
3. One 25-30 min. walk using metronome in different cadences, choosing two focuses and remembering to level your pelvis as you twist at pivot point
4. One 30 min.+ walk: The Focusing Walk

Post Walk Stretches:
calf stretch, achilles stretch, hip flexor stretch, hamstring stretch, adductor stretch, quadriceps stretch, **latissimus dorsi (lats) stretch**

Program Development: Review your vision, assessment, goals, & current Program. Consider working with a buddy.

What to re-read in the book: Chapter 3, pages 48-59; Chapter 4, pages 67, 89-95; and Chapter 5, pages 126-129 (The Focusing Walk).

What to re-view on DVD: Lesson Three: Upper Body Focuses.
Watch the DVD on the first workout of this week, then, if necessary, at the start of your second and third workout for reinforcement.

Write in the days and times for your 4 sessions this week:

Workout #1	Workout #2	Workout #3	Workout #4
Day _____	Day _____	Day _____	Day _____
Time _____	Time _____	Time _____	Time _____

THEME OF THE WEEK

Cadence and Arm Swing - Balance Between Upper and Lower Body

This week you'll be working on cadence, arm swing, and how the motion of your upper body helps balance out the motion of your lower body. You've already been mindful of your stride length in past workouts, so now you're going to add the focus on cadence as well, testing out different speeds (different cadences) with the help of a metronome. In fact, using a metronome (described on page 67 in the book) as a training tool will help you match your stride to a steady beat to keep your cadence consistent. Swing your arms along with the metronome and move forward as a single, fluid unit.

What's cadence again? Think of cadence as a rhythm, which, after all, is what makes the world go around. Your cadence is the number of strides taken by one of your legs each minute. Tuning into your cadence is a great way to make your walking more efficient and enjoyable. You'll learn how to change cadence relative to how fast you want to walk.

Before you begin each walk this week, practice your arm swing in front of a mirror to check that your arms are bent correctly—not crossing your centerline—and that your shoulders are relaxed. Make a Choice to walk leading with your upper body as your lower body relaxes. Also, Make a Choice to maintain balance between your upper and lower body. During your walks, remain mindful of that T12/L1 point where your spine twists. When your spine twists at this point, more chi energy will enter your body. Your flexibility relative to this T12/L1 point is thus essential to the fluid flow of your chi, which energizes you while you walk.

> *You use your arms to create balance between your upper and lower body. You'll move more efficiently when all parts are working together. When your upper and lower body move fluidly—in a balanced, flexible manner—no part of your body will offer any hindrance to your forward motion.*

You've got four walks on your agenda this week, the last of which will be the Focusing Walk from the ChiWalking Matrix (Appendix C, pg. 194 of this workbook). Plan to complete all four walks, even if you can't do all of them for as long as suggested. As we've been reminding you, continue to listen to your body, perform body scans throughout your days, and really sense that T12/L1 center of your twist when you walk and rotate your spine.

CHI-SKILL OF THE WEEK

Flexibility

(Read pages 48-51 of the book.)
Another one of the key Chi-Skills is flexibility. Because humans are very adaptable organisms, we're meant to continually evolve and develop at a much more sophisticated and higher rate than other organisms. And in order to do so, we must be able to adapt quickly. That, of course, entails being flexible—the more flexible you are (in mind and body), the more quickly you can handle whatever comes your way, either from the road or from life itself.

A flexible mind is one that listens to the body and makes adjustments accordingly. ChiWalking is about mind *and* body. Not mind *over* body.

Last week you focused on your Needle in Cotton, which should have helped you gather your energy (your chi) to your center and relax everything else. Now that you are practicing that, you're going to take notice of your flexibility so you can really let that freely flowing chi flow even more easily. Flexibility, by the way, isn't just about loose joints, stretching, bending and twisting. It's about moving as a fluid unit, relaxing, balancing…setting your body in a motion that coordinates all body components smoothly, elegantly. It engages the mind, too.

> *When your muscles, ligaments, and tendons are relaxed and flexible, blood, oxygen, and chi can flow unobstructed through your body, making exercise much easier on your heart, lungs, and other systems.*

Axial twisting is a form of flexibility, and as you become aware of it in your body, you'll gain greater flexibility in more than just your physical being. Remember, flexibility in form, flexibility in life!

WORKOUT #1

Today's Date: _____

LESSON: 6 MINUTES

• Watch Lesson 3, Part 1: Head Position

• Watch Lesson 3, Part 2: Arm Swing: How to Swing Your Arms

• Follow along with the DVD and practice both your head position and arm swing

PRE-WALK BODY LOOSENERS: 5 Minutes

Use either the DVD to review your body looseners and learn the new one for this week (Grounding Stance), or refer to the book (pages 142-155).

• Begin by shaking out your whole body like you're a rag doll. Be sure to shake your arms and legs thoroughly. Have fun with this. Really *shake* out your entire body. Feel your head, neck, shoulders, arms, hands, torso, abdomen, legs, and feet cut loose. Let it all go!

Then, do the following exercises:
• ankle rolls, knee circles, hip circles, sacrum circles, pelvic rotation, spine rolls, spinal twist, **grounding stance:** hold for 30 seconds**.**

Shake out that body again. FEEL your physical being from the top of your head all the way down to your toes.

Learn Post-Walk Stretches: *5 Minutes*
• Refer to Appendix B. New stretch this week: **latissimus dorsi (lats) stretch** (Add this one to your previous repertoire.)

MAKE A CHOICE!

Stand in front of a mirror and practice your arm swing. Your hands should never cross your centerline. Keep your fingers lightly curled in. Then check your head position—eyes level, chin tucked.

MOVE FORWARD INTO YOUR WALK: 25-30 MINUTES

Set your watch so it beeps every minute. Use those one-minute reminders to remain mindful in the practice and tune into your focuses.

FOCUSES DURING THE WALK

• First 5 minutes: Warm up at a strolling pace. Practice your head position and focus on arm swing.

• Next 20-25 minutes: Using your metronome, cycle through 3 arm swing positions (slow, medium, and fast pace walking), holding each position for 8 minutes at a time. As you're going through the 3 walking cadences, be very aware of that pivot point at T12/L1, from which you rotate your lower body.

*Metronome settings:

1st Phase: 55-60 spm

2nd Phase: 60-65 spm

3rd Phase: 65-70 spm

• Last 5 minutes: Cool down at a strolling pace. Feel the effects of your walk. Make sure you continue to relax your lower legs and pick up your heels.

POST WALK STRETCHES: 5 Minutes

Do your calf, achilles, hip flexor, hamstring, adductor, quadriceps, and **lats stretches**.

✳ SEE YOU WHEN YOU GET BACK! ✳

END OF WALK REVIEW: 5 MINUTES

Welcome back.

How many minutes did you walk?_____

Could you sense your fluidity as you swung your arms with your strides?

_____

_____

With each stride, could you feel your legs straightening behind you at a comfortable stride length and cadence?

_____

_____

Could you feel your T12/L1 pivot as you walked in all cadences?

_____

Did your body feel balanced, and moving forward in a single, fluid unit?

_____

_____

Is there anything you learned during today's walk? (Any realizations or understandings?) What were they?

_____

_____

_____

_____

_____

_____

Optional (for first workout of the week):
Resting heart rate (RHR): _____beats per minute.

PROGRAM DEVELOPMENT: 15 Minutes

Review Your Vision and Self Assesment:
Go to Appendix A: Program Development Week 5, Part 1

FOCUSES IN BETWEEN WORKOUTS

Whenever you're sitting or driving a car, hold your head in the correct postural position. (Remember the head-straightening scene from the DVD? Reach for the sky with the crown of your head!)

RE-NEW YOUR COMMITMENT

I will do another ChiWalking workout on this day:_____
(Write this date down on your calendar or in any daily planner you keep.)

WORKOUT #2

Today's Date: _____

LESSON: 5 MINUTES

• Watch Lesson 3, Part 3: Shoulder Position

• Practice correct shoulder positioning along with the DVD

Time-Out for a Body Scan!
Before doing your pre-walk looseners today, take a minute or two to practice body sensing by conducting a full body sweep. Start at your feet and end at the top of your head. Anything tight? Sore? Tingly? Be mindful of every sensation moving through you right now. Be mindful of tense areas to address during Body Looseners.

PRE-WALK BODY LOOSENERS: 5 Minutes

(Refer to the DVD or pages 142-155.)
• Begin by shaking out your whole body like you're a rag doll. Be sure to shake your arms and legs thoroughly. Have fun with this. Shake your head, neck, shoulders, arms, hands, torso, legs, and feet. Let it all go!

• Then do your ankle rolls, knee circles, hip circles, sacrum circles, pelvic rotations, spine rolls, spinal twists, and **grounding stance.**

> *Take a moment to FEEL every square inch of your body. Shake it out again if you like!*

If you need to, review Post-Walk Stretches: 2 Minutes
(Refer to Appendix B to review the calf stretch, achilles stretch, hip flexor, hamstring stretch, adductor stretch, quadriceps stretch, and **lats stretch**.)

MAKE A CHOICE!

Before starting your walk today, practice your arm swing in front of a mirror. Your hands should never cross your centerline. Keep your fingers lightly curled in. Then check your head position—eyes level, chin tucked.

MOVE FORWARD INTO YOUR WALK: 25-30 MINUTES

Now you're ready to get walking. Set your watch for one-minute intervals. Snap on that metronome. When your watch sounds off, check in on your posture, and your focuses.

FOCUSES DURING THE WALK

• First 2 minutes: Warm up at a slow pace. Get your head and shoulders aligned properly.

• Next 8 minutes: Walk at various cadences. Use your metronome and practice your arm swing at different paces (slow, medium, and fast pace).

• Next 20 minutes: Choose a brisk, but sustainable cadence and focus on walking with your **statue tilting forward** and your **elbows swinging back**.

• Last 5 minutes: Cool down at a strolling pace. Feel your upper body forward over your support legs with each step.

> *Remember to keep feeling your statue tilting while your legs sweep out the back in short strides. Feel your center of gravity and your balance forward. The center of your twist is at T-12/L-1, where Chi enters the body!*

POST WALK STRETCHES: 5 Minutes

Do your calf, achilles, hip flexor, hamstring, adductor, quadriceps, and **lats stretches**.

✳ SEE YOU WHEN YOU GET BACK! ✳

END OF WALK REVIEW: 5 MINUTES

How many minutes did you walk? _____.

Did you sense your fluidity as you swung your arms with your strides?

_____

_____

Did positioning your head and shoulders in the correct posture come naturally?

_____

With each stride, could you feel your legs straightening behind you at a comfortable stride length and cadence?

_____

_____

Were you able to follow the metronome's beats easily? Which pace was most difficult?

_____

_____

Could you feel your lower body relax as you moved forward and focused on upper body flexibility?

_____

_____

Could you feel your pivot point as you walked in all cadences?

_____

_____

Is there anything you learned during today's walk? (Any realizations or understandings?) What were they?

_____

_____

_____

_____

FOCUSES IN BETWEEN WORKOUTS

Continue to check in on your **posture**. Keep your **head in the correct postural position**. Whether you're in front of the computer screen, driving, walking, or eating dinner; take time-out to **Body Scan** and let go of any tension. You might find, for example, that your shoulders are tight and rising up toward your ears as you work at a desk or respond to e-mails. Let loose!

RE-NEW YOUR COMMITMENT

*I will do another ChiWalking workout on this day:*_____
(Write this date down on your calendar or in any daily planner you keep.)

WORKOUT #3

Today's Date: _____

REVIEW: 5 MINUTES (optional)

- Watch Lesson 3, Part 1-3: Head Position, Arm Swing, and Shoulder Position again on the DVD (if you need to)
- Body Looseners for the week
- Post-Walk Stretches for the week

PRE-WALK BODY LOOSENERS: 5 Minutes

- Shake out your entire body from head to toe. Let loose!
- Take a minute to Body Scan. Relax and breathe into any tight areas before you loosen up!
- Do your ankle rolls, knee circles, hip circles, sacrum circles, and pelvic rotations, spine rolls, spinal twists, and grounding stance.

> *Take a moment to FEEL every square inch of your body.*
> *Inhale a big, deep breath that fills your lungs from the bottom up and pushes out your belly.*
> *Then exhale completely, relaxing your chest first.*

MAKE A CHOICE!

Choose to always have your upper body moving forward while your elbows and legs swing to the rear.

MOVE FORWARD INTO YOUR WALK: 25-30 MINUTES

Make an intention to do a full 25-30 minutes today if you haven't made it that long yet. You're going to repeat what you did in your last workout, focusing also on leveling your pelvis and rotatiing at your pivot point. Set your countdown timer for one-minute intervals and snap on your metronome!

FOCUSES DURING THE WALK

• First 2 minutes: Warm up at a slow pace. Align your **head and shoulders.**

• Next 8 minutes: Use your metronome at **different paces** (slow, medium, and fast) and practice your arm swing.

• Next 20 minutes: Choose a brisk and sustainable cadence and focus on **tilting your statue** with your **elbows swinging to the rear.** If you would like a challenge, you can also focus on **leveling your pelvis** and **rotating at your pivot point.**

• Last 5 minutes: Cool down at a strolling pace. Feel your **upper body forward** over your support leg with each step.

POST WALK STRETCHES: 5 Minutes

Do your calf, achilles, hip flexor, hamstring, adductor, quadriceps, and **lats stretches**.

✳ SEE YOU WHEN YOU GET BACK! ✳

END OF WALK REVIEW: 5 MINUTES

How many minutes did you walk? _____.

Can you feel how the three different arm positons effect your energy level when you walk?

_____

_____

Can you feel how keeping your chin tucked effects your posture and momentum?

_____

With each stride, could you feel your legs straightening behind you at a comfortable stride length *and* cadence?

_____

Write down the cadence you felt to be brisk but sustainable.

_____

_____

_____

Could you feel your pivot point as you walked in all cadences?

_____

_____

How well were you able to focus on leveling your pelvis while rotating at your pivot point?

_____

Is there anything you learned during today's walk? (Any realizations or understandings?) What were they?

_____

_____

_____

_____

_____

FOCUSES IN BETWEEN WORKOUTS

Continue to check in on your **posture**. Keep your **head in the correct postural position**. Whether you're in front of the computer screen, driving, walking, eating dinner… Take time-out to **Body Scan** and let go of any tension. You might find, for example, that your shoulders are tight and rising up toward your ears as you work at a desk or respond to e-mails. Take a deep breath and drop your shoulders while you exhale. . . as often as possible.

RE-NEW YOUR COMMITMENT

*I will do another ChiWalking workout on this day:*_____
(Write this date down on your calendar or in any daily planner you keep.)

WORKOUT #4

Today's Date: _____

REVIEW: 5 MINUTES (optional)

• Watch Lesson 3 again on the DVD (if you need to)
• Body Looseners for the week
• Post-Walk Stretches for the week

PRE-WALK BODY LOOSENERS: 5 Minutes

• Shake out your entire body from head to toe. Let loose!

• Take a minute to Body Scan. Tend to any tight areas.

• Then do your ankle rolls, knee circles, hip circles, sacrum circles, and pelvic rotations, spine rolls, spinal twists, and **grounding stance**.

Take a moment to FEEL every square inch of your body.
Inhale a big, deep breath that fills your lungs from the bottom up
and pushes out your belly.
Then, exhale completely, relaxing your chest first.

MOVE FORWARD INTO YOUR WALK: 25-30 MINUTES

The Focusing Walk

This is your fourth walk this week (hurray!). Today you're going to do one of the walks from the ChiWalking Matrix (Appendix C): The Focusing Walk. Plan to spend at least 30 minutes on this walk, and feel free to extend it to 45 minutes if you feel up to it. Set your countdown timer for one-minute intervals so you stay mindful in the practice. See pages 126-129 in the book for various types of focusing walks. Today we're going to practice Focus Walk: Eyes on the Horizon (Pg. 127 in the book). The focuses are below.

FOCUSES DURING THE WALK

• First 5 minutes: Begin walking at an slow and relaxing pace, keeping your stride comfortable and short. Find a place to walk that is flat, smooth and relatively unobstructed.

• Next 20-30 minutes: Bring your speed up to a medium, but still relaxing pace. Set your countdown timer to beep at one-minute intervals. Pick an object in the distance and start your timer. Keep your eyes focused on that object while you walk toward it for one minute. Try not to break your gaze during your timed minute. When your watch beeps, take a one minute break until it beeps again. Then, find another object in the distance and fix your gaze on that while you walk toward it for the next minute. Repeat this on/off cycle for the duration of your walk. If you want to, add focuses of your choosing in 1-minute intervals.

• Last 5-10 minutes: Cool down at a strolling pace.

POST WALK STRETCHES: 5 Minutes

Do your calf, achilles, hip flexor, hamstring, adductor, quadriceps, and **lats stretches**.

✳ SEE YOU WHEN YOU GET BACK! ✳

END OF WALK REVIEW: 5 MINUTES

How many minutes did you walk? _____

How well do you think you maintained your posture during your Focusing Walk?

_____

_____

Did you find this walk to be relaxing for your mind while you continued to focus?

_____

_____

_____

Did you maintain the same cadence throughout the walk for the most part?

_____

_____

Were you able to hold an unbroken visual focus during any of the one-minute intervals?

_____

_____

_____

Did you feel like you were moving as a fluid unit, while focusing with your eyes?

_____

_____

Is there anything you learned during today's walk? (Any realizations or understandings?)
What were they?

_____

_____

_____

_____

_____

PROGRAM DEVELOPMENT: 15 Minutes

Walking With A Buddy:
Go to Appendix A: Program Development Week 5, Part 2

Congratulations on finishing Week 5! Take a deep belly breath and do a quick body scan before closing out today's workout. Take a moment to sense how you feel inside and out, from your mind to your muscles.

Now get your calendar out and plan next week's walks.

FOCUSES IN BETWEEN WORKOUTS

Get Aligned. Pick Up Your Heels.
Gather Your Center…
Let Everything Else Relax.

RE-NEW YOUR COMMITMENT

I will start ChiWalking WEEK 6 on this day:_____
(Write this date down on your calendar or in any daily planner you keep.)

WEEK 6 OVERVIEW

Theme of the Week: Putting It All Together

Chi-Skill: Breathing

Minimum Time Commitment: 5 x 45-minute workouts, 4.5 total hours

Body Looseners: ankle rolls, knee circles, hip circles, sacrum circles, pelvic rotations, spine rolls, spinal twist, shoulders and upper back, grounding stance

5 Walks: Smooth and flat terrain

    1. Walking Test: 20 minutes, flat, smooth terrain

    2. 30-40 min. walk repeating cycles of focuses - **Form Focus Walk**

    3. 25-40 min. walk - **Hilly Walk**

    4. 40-50 min. walk repeating cycles of focuses - **Form Focus Walk**

    5. 30+ min. walk - **The Energizing Walk**

Post Walk Stretches:
calf stretch, achilles stretch, hip flexor stretch, hamstring stretch, adductor stretch, quadriceps stretch, lats, **leg drains**

Program Development: Creating Your Own Walks

What to re-read in the book:
Chapter 2, page 36-38 ("Step 5: Move Forward")
Chapter 3, pages 51-55 ("Breathing")
Chapter 4, pages 96-100 ("Taking Your First Chi Walking Steps")
Chapter 5, pages 125-126 (The Energizing Walk)

What to re-view on DVD: Lesson Four: Let's Go Walking
Watch the DVD lesson on the first workout of this week, then, if necessary, at the start of your remaining workouts for reinforcement.

Write in the days and times for your 5 sessions this week:

Workout #1	Workout #2	Workout #3	Workout #4	Workout #5
Day _____	Day _____	Day _____	Day _____	Day _____
Time _____	Time _____	Time _____	Time _____	Time _____

Move Forward: Putting it All Together

At this point you've been through the majority of the basic ChiWalking principles and techniques. You've practiced posture, upper and lower body focuses, cadence, and stride length. You have been introduced to the whole form and are working to bring the upper and lower body focuses together. You have been practicing the first four steps: Get Aligned, Engage Your Core, Create Balance, and Make A Choice. Now, under the guidance of the fifth mindful step, it's time to put it all together and Move Forward with everything you've learned so far.

Your body moves more efficiently when all parts are working in synch and balance. This week you'll practice what you've learned by maintaining different focuses in 5-minute intervals while moving at a slightly quicker pace than usual. Practice just a few focuses at a time. After years of walking, I still do this. Some days I focus only on my cadence, others days I focus on improving my alignment. Over time you'll experience more and more days when everything comes together and it feels like you're gliding. Give it time and keep working on the individual focuses. You'll be amazed at what happens.

This week you'll also work on the fourth Chi-Skill: breathing. Improving your breathing will help you stay calm and focused while your body becomes energized by the fresh air you take in. Give yourself some time to practice breathing in this new way. Bringing air deep into your lungs energizes your body and spirit.

Over the past 5 weeks, you've followed a program that keeps Gradual Progress in mind, slowly adding more distance and skills. This week you'll begin to create your own walks following the same principle. You'll choose your own focuses, and begin to tailor your own custom program.

> *Find the "Sweet Spot" over and over again with every breath as you walk. Your upper body is directly over your hips while walking. You're tilting your statue and rotating at your pivot point, creating balance between your upper body (tilted forward) and lower body (legs out the back).*

Breathing

(Pages 51-55 of the book.)
Even though breathing is an automatic function of the body (you don't have to tell yourself to breathe), it is important to breathe correctly in order to maximize the exchange of air/oxygen for blood/oxygen with each breath. Start by aligning your posture (especially your upper body). Relax your shoulders and then practice "belly breathing". Blow all the air out of your lungs by pursing your lips and pulling your belly button in towards your spine. Once your lungs are empty, relax your abdominal muscles, and fill your lungs completely from the bottom up. Notice how your stomach expands outward. Proper breathing will help keep your energy (chi) flowing, your muscles fresh, and your mind working well. The brain is, after all, very dependent on the air you breathe. The better you breath, the better you can focus.

If you've been walking regularly for the past 6 weeks, you've most likely increased your aerobic capacity from the level at which you started. This is one of the wonderful results of ChiWalking. Mindful breathing will increase your aerobic capacity and make it easier to add increasingly challenging walks into your program. It will also keep you very much in the present moment, which is where real choice happens.

WORKOUT #1

Today's Date: _____

LESSON: 5 MINUTES

• Watch Lesson 4 on the DVD: Let's go Walking

PRE-WALK BODY LOOSENERS: 5 Minutes

Review the body looseners on your DVD, or refer to the book *(pages 142-155)*. Do all of your looseners, finishing with the **Grounding Stance**.

• Before starting your body looseners, shake out your whole body, like a dog that just walked out of a lake. Pay special attention to shaking your arms and legs. Let it all go! Now do a Body Scan. Really feel each part of our body.

Then, do the following exercises:

• Ankle rolls: Do 10 clockwise circles and then 10 counter-clockwise. Switch legs and re-peat the exercise.

• Knee Circles: Do 10 clockwise circles and then 10 counter-clockwise circles.

• Hip Circles: Do 10 clockwise circles and then 10 counter-clockwise circles.

• Sacrum Circles: Do 10 clockwise circles and then 10 counter-clockwise circles.

• Pelvic Rotations: Do a few rotations with left leg back. . . then right leg back.

• Spine Rolls: Do 3 repeats.

• Spinal Twist: Do 3 repeats.

• Shoulders and Upper Back: Do 10 with right leg back, 10 with left leg back.

• **Grounding Stance**: Hold for 30-60 seconds.

Learn Post-Walk Stretches: 5 Minutes
• Review your post-walk stretches by referring to Appendix B in this workbook . This week's addition will be **leg drains** (add this to your previous repertoire).

*Remember: You've learned all the stretching exercises now. Stretching is just as important as your walk, so make time for it. End your stretching session with the Grounding Stance before moving on to your next activity.

MAKE A CHOICE!

Take a few deep, belly breaths. If you start with a loose, relaxed body, you'll be able to really get the most out of your focuses.

20-MINUTE WALKING TEST

For your first walk this week, we'd like you to do another walking test, like the one you did in Week 2. This is a check in to see "how far you've come" in the past 4 weeks (page 185-186 in the book). Today, simply walk and gauge your health, energy, and attitude. The results from this walk will provide a comparison for measuring your progress since Week 2. The assessment you make this week will help you see your current level of conditioning and will help you to design your own ChiWalking program.

RULES OF THE ROAD FOR COMPLETING YOUR 20-MINUTE WALKING TEST

- Walk on a flat surface. Try to follow the same route you took for your first Walk Test.
- Monitor your heart rate manually, or use a heart-rate monitor if you have one.
- Warm up for 5 minutes, then check your watch and walk for 20 minutes at a pace that is fast for you (generally over 65 spm). You can use your metronome here.
- Upon returning, do three things:
    - Take your pulse immediately* (or look at your monitor).
    - Note how many minutes you walked.
    - On a scale of 1-10, what was your perceived level of exertion? Take note of it.

You'll have space in your End of Walk Review to write down your findings, do it right after checking your pulse so that you don't forget the number!

POST WALK STRETCHES: 5 Minutes

Do your Calf, Achilles, Hip Flexor, Hamstring, Adductor, Quadricep, Lats, and Leg Drains.

✳ SEE YOU WHEN YOU GET BACK! ✳

END OF WALK REVIEW: 5 MINUTES

Welcome back. Devote these last 5 minutes to jotting down a few personal notes.

Your heart rate at the end of your 20-minute walk test_____

Compare your heart rate to your first walk test_____

On a scale of 1-10, what was your perceived level of exertion?_____

How did this test compare to your first test? Was it easier? Did you feel a difference?

_____

_____

_____

_____

Were you able to easily maintain a quick pace? _____

_____

Could you find the Sweet Spot where everything is aligned properly and balanced with your upper body leaning forward and your legs sweeping out the back?

_____

_____

Could you sense the fluidity between your upper and lower body as you moved forward?

_____

_____

Were you able to feel your spine twisting at your pivot point? _____

_____

_____

Optional (for the first workout of the week):
Resting heart rate (RHR):_____beats per minute.

PROGRAM DEVELOPMENT: 10 Minutes

Choosing Your Own Focuses for the Rest of this Week
Go to Appendix A, Program Development, Week 6, Part 1

FOCUSES IN BETWEEN WORKOUTS

Belly Breathing is easy to focus on no matter what you're doing—walking, sitting, talking, shopping, working, driving, etc. You have to breathe all day long, so why not make it as mindful as you can. One of the best places to practice is just before falling asleep at night. When you're lying on your back, feel your belly rise and fall with each breath, not your chest! This is also good to do first thing in the morning when you're lying in bed just after waking up. Just don't fall back to sleep!

RE-NEW YOUR COMMITMENT

I will do another ChiWalking workout on this day: _____
(Write this date down on your calendar or in any daily planner you keep.)

WORKOUT #2

Today's Date: _____

LESSON: 5 MINUTES

• Watch Lesson 4: Let's Go Walking, for review.

PRE-WALK BODY LOOSENERS: 5 Minutes

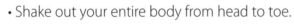
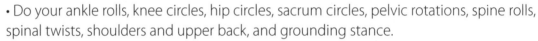

(Refer to the DVD or pages 142-155 in the book, as needed)

• Shake out your entire body from head to toe.

• Do your ankle rolls, knee circles, hip circles, sacrum circles, pelvic rotations, spine rolls, spinal twists, shoulders and upper back, and grounding stance.

Do a Body Scan
Take 5 deep-belly-breathing breaths! Then, do a 60 second Body Scan. Find the tension and let it dissolve with another deep breath.

Review Post-Walk Stretches: *2 Minutes*
(Review Appendix B if necessary.)

MAKE A CHOICE!

Go back to the list of focuses. Review each pair of focuses you chose to practice for this walk. If you're unsure about any of the focuses, go back to the DVD and watch the section that covers the focus in question. Once you're clear on which focuses you'll be practicing, MAKE A CHOICE to concentrate on each of your chosen pairs of focuses during this walk. Follow the instructions provided for help.

MOVE FORWARD INTO YOUR WALK: 25-40 MINUTES

Set your watch for 5-minute intervals. Grab your metronome and set your cadence to medium (60-65 spm).

FOCUSES DURING YOUR WALK:

• First 5 minutes: Warm up at a strolling pace. Practice your belly breathing. Try to get your breathing in synch with your strides.

• Next 20-35 minutes: Walk at a medium pace (60-65 spm) while alternating between the upper body focuses and the lower body focus you chose. Start your countdown timer and go through your walk changing focuses every 5 minutes. Then, do both focuses together. Go back and repeat the same progression with the same focuses, or do the same progression with two new focuses. For a real challenge try to hold all 4 focuses in the last five minutes.

• Last 5 minutes: Cool down at a strolling pace. Feel the effects of your walk on your entire body—from head to toe.

POST WALK STRETCHES: 5 Minutes

Do your calf, achilles, hip flexor, hamstring, adductor, quadriceps, lats, and leg drains. Follow with the **grounding stance**.

✷ SEE YOU WHEN YOU GET BACK! ✷

END OF WALK REVIEW: 5 MINUTES

Welcome back.

How many minutes did you walk?_____.

Which pairs of focuses—upper and lower body—did you choose?

_____

_____

Is there any focus you feel you still don't quite understand, or need additional practice with?

_____

_____

Which focuses—upper or lower—were more of a challenge for you?

_____

_____

How well were you able to combine all four focuses at one time?

_____

Could you feel fluidity between your upper and lower body as you moved forward?

_____

With each stride, could you feel your legs straightening behind you at a comfortable stride length and cadence?

_____

How well could you sense your pivot point location (T12/L1)?

_____

Is there anything you learned during today's walk? (Any realizations or understandings?) What were they?

_____

_____

_____

FOCUSES IN BETWEEN WORKOUTS

Keep focusing on your Belly Breathing wherever you go. Also, check in so that you can feel your T12/L1 pivot point as frequently as possible.

RE-NEW YOUR COMMITMENT

I will I will do another ChiWalking workout on this day: _____
(Write this date down on your calendar or in any daily planner you keep.)

WORKOUT #3

Today's Date: _____

LESSON: 5 MINUTES

• Watch Lesson 4 on the DVD: Let's Go Walking

PRE-WALK BODY LOOSENERS: 5 Minutes

(Refer to the DVD or pages 142-155 in the book, as needed)

• Shake out your entire body from head to toe.

• Do your ankle rolls, knee circles, hip circles, sacrum circles, pelvic rotations, spine rolls, spinal twists, shoulders and upper back, and **grounding stance**.

Take a moment to FEEL every square inch of your body. Shake it out again if you like!

Review Post-walk stretches: *2 minutes*
(Review Appendix B if necessary.)

MAKE A CHOICE!

The Hilly Walk *(read pages 108-112 in the book)*
If there are hills in your area and you are so inclined, you can use this walk to practice your hill walking technique. Or, see the walk you chose on page 181 of this workbook. With a little practice, you can learn how to walk uphill more efficiently and reduce impact to your legs while walking downhill. The trick to walking uphill is swinging your arms *forward* instead of to the rear (as you do on flat terrain) and shortening your stride to keep your legs from overworking.

MOVE FORWARD INTO YOUR WALK: 25 to 30 MINUTES

Find a hilly area (not steep) and begin by warming up on flat terrain for 5 minutes. Once you feel warmed up, head up your first hill.

FOCUSES DURING YOUR WALK:

• **Next 25-30 Minutes:** Practice the following focuses depending on whether you are going uphill or downhill.

• **Uphill:** Shorten your stride and bend your arms 90º. If you get tired walking up hill, you can either shorten your stride or turn around and head back down. As long as you're walking uphill, you should be swinging your arms forward with your hands swinging up toward your chin. Tilt your statue forward when walking uphill and starighten your rear legs behind you with each step.

• **Downhill:** Level your pelvis and let it really rotate as you walk downhill. Roll heel-to-toe with your feet and keep your posture vertical, not tilted forward. Let your arms swing easliy at your sides. Keep your stride at a comfortable length.

POST WALK STRETCHES: 5 Minutes

Do your calf, achilles, hip flexor, hamstring, adductor, quadricep, lats, and leg drains.

✳ **SEE YOU WHEN YOU GET BACK!** ✳

END OF WALK REVIEW: 5 MINUTES

Welcome back.

How many minutes did you walk?_____

Which pairs of focuses—upper and lower body—did you choose?

_____

_____

Which focuses—uphill or downhill—were more of a challenge for you?

_____

_____

When you combined focuses, could you feel the relationship between your upper and lower body as you moved forward?

_____

With each uphill stride, could you feel your legs straightening behind you at a comfortable stride length?

_____

Did you shorten your stride on the uphills?_____

Is there anything you learned during today's walk? (Any realizations or understandings?) What were they?

_____

_____

_____

_____

FOCUSES IN BETWEEN WORKOUTS

Keep focusing on your Belly Breathing wherever you go. Also, check in so that you can feel your T12/L1 pivot point as frequently as possible. You can practice "pivoting" in your desk chair.

RE-NEW YOUR COMMITMENT

I will do another ChiWalking workout on this day: _____
(Write this date down on your calendar or in any daily planner you keep.)

WORKOUT #4

Today's Date: _____

LESSON: 5 MINUTES

• Watch Lesson 4: Let's Go Walking

PRE-WALK BODY LOOSENERS: 5 Minutes

(Refer to the DVD or pages 142-155 in the book, as needed)

• Shake out your entire body from head to toe.

• Do your ankle rolls, knee circles, hip circles, sacrum circles, pelvic rotations, spine rolls, spinal twists, shoulders and upper back, and grounding stance.

Take a moment to FEEL every square inch of your body. Shake it out again if you like!

Review Post-Walk Stretches: *2 Minutes*
(Review Appendix B if necessary.)

MAKE A CHOICE!

Go back to the list of focuses you picked to practice during this walk. If you're unsure of any of the focuses, go back to the DVD and watch the section that covers the focus in question. Once you're clear on what you'll be practicing, MAKE A CHOICE to concentrate on each of your chosen pairs of focuses during this walk by following the instructions to follow.

MOVE FORWARD INTO YOUR WALK: 25-40 MINUTES

Set your watch for 5-minute intervals. Grab your metronome and set your cadence to medium (60-65 spm).

FOCUSES DURING YOUR WALK:

• First 5 minutes: Warm up at a strolling pace. Practice your belly breathing. Try to get your breathing in synch with your strides.

• Next 20-35 minutes: Walk at a medium pace (60-65 spm) while alternating between the upper body focus and the lower body focus you chose. Start your countdown timer and go through your walk changing focuses every 5 minutes. Then, do both focuses together. Go back and repeat the same progression with the same focuses, or do the same progression with two new focuses. For a real challenge try to hold all 4 focuses in the last five minutes.

• Last 5 minutes: Cool down at a strolling pace. Feel the effects of your walk on your entire body—from head to toe.

POST WALK STRETCHES: 5 Minutes

Do your calf, achilles, hip flexor, hamstring, adductor, quadriceps, lats, and leg drains. Follow with the **Grounding Stance**.

✱ SEE YOU WHEN YOU GET BACK! ✱

END OF WALK REVIEW: 5 MINUTES

Welcome back.

How many minutes did you walk?_____

Which pairs of focuses—upper and lower body—did you choose?

_____

_____

Write down the focuses that help you the most

_____

_____

Which focuses—upper or lower—were more of a challenge for you?

_____

_____

If you tried, how well were you able to combine all four focuses at one time?

_____

_____

When you combined both pairs of focuses, could you feel any fluidity between your upper and lower body as you moved forward?

_____

Can you feel the tilt of your statue? Can you feel how it helps move you forward?

_____

Is there anything you learned during today's walk? (Any realizations or understandings?) What were they?

_____

_____

_____

_____

FOCUSES IN BETWEEN WORKOUTS

Keep focusing on your Belly Breathing wherever you go. Also, check in so that you can feel your T12/L1 pivot point as frequently as possible.

RE-NEW YOUR COMMITMENT

I will do another ChiWalking workout on this day:_____
(Write this date down on your calendar or in any daily planner you keep.)

WORKOUT #5

Today's Date: _____

MOVE FORWARD INTO YOUR WALK:

Energizing Walk

For your fifth walk this week you'll learn the **Energizing Walk** from the Matrix. It's a helpful walk to have under your belt for when you need it, and it's one of our favorites. You'll come back ready to take on whatever's next, in a vibrant and centered way. (See pages 125 and 126 of the book.) Choose a location away from busy streets. A park or a trail is ideal. This walk is best done alone because you'll be doing visualization and breathing exercises, both of which require your focused attention for the entire time you're walking. This workout is just for you. If you have the time, plan to walk for an hour. You'll love it.

FOCUSES DURING YOUR WALK:

• First 5 minutes: Begin walking at a slow and relaxing pace, keeping your **stride comfortable and short**. If you can, try to **breathe deeply through your nose.**

• Next 20-30 minutes: Bring your speed up to a medium/brisk pace (60-70 spm). Continue to **breathe in and out through your nose**. Begin this visualization: energy moving up the back of your spine from your tailbone to the top of your head on your in-breath, and flowing down the front side of your spine to your pubic bone on your out-breath. Try to hold this focus for the entire allotted time. Set your beeper to go off every 10 minutes so that it can remind you to focus on what you're doing.

• Last 5-10 minutes: Cool down at a strolling pace. Concentrate on relaxed breathing without the visualization.

POST WALK STRETCHES: 5 Minutes

Do your calf, achilles, hip flexor, hamstring, adductor, quadriceps, lats, and leg drains. Follow with the **Grounding Stance.**

 ✳ **SEE YOU WHEN YOU GET BACK!** ✳

113

WORKOUT #5 WEEK 6 - PUTTING IT ALL TOGETHER

END OF WALK REVIEW: 5 MINUTES

Welcome back.

How many minutes did you walk?_____.

Were you able to get a rhythmical connection between your breathing and your cadence? Was it comfortable to breathe through your nose?

_____

How did your body feel when you finished your walk? (Energized, refreshed, unchanged?)

_____
_____
_____

Were you able to visualize the flow of energy up the back of your spine and down the front of your spine?

_____

How well were you able to combine your walking focuses with your visualization practice?

_____

Did you find it helpful to have your beeper remind you to return to your focus?

_____

Is there anything you learned during today's walk? (Any realizations or understandings?) What were they?

_____
_____
_____
_____

PROGRAM DEVELOPMENT: 15 Minutes

Create your walks for Week 7
Go to Appendix A, Program Development, Week 6, Part 2

Congratulations on finishing Week 6!
Take a moment to sense how you feel inside and out,
from your mind to your muscles.

FOCUSES IN BETWEEN WORKOUTS

Between now and your next workout, take some time out to focus on posture and form. Whenever you're walking, check on your breathing, and the balance you create between your upper and lower body as you move forward. Keep the feeling of that T12/L1 pivot point close to your mind. Visualize that Needle in Cotton.

RE-NEW YOUR COMMITMENT

I will start Week 7 on this day: _____
(Write this date down on your calendar or in any daily planner you keep.)

WEEK 7 OVERVIEW

Theme of the Week: New Terrain

Chi-Skill: Non-Identification

Minimum Time Commitment: 5 workouts, 4.5 hours total

Body Looseners: ankle rolls, knee circles, hip circles, sacrum circles, pelvic rotations, spine rolls, spinal twist, shoulders and upper back, grounding stance

5 Walks: Picking up the pace and walking various terrains

1. 25-40 minutes: **Form Focus Walk**
2. 30-40 mins: **Speed Workout**
3. 30-40 mins: **Cardio Walk**
4. 45-60 mins: **Aerobic/Long Walk**
5. 30+ mins: **The Grounding Walk**

Post Walk Stretches:
calf stretch, achilles stretch, hip flexor stretch, hamstring stretch, adductor stretch, quadriceps stretch, lats, leg drains

What to re-read in the book:
Chapter 3, pages 181-182 ("Non-identification")
Chapter 5, pages 123-124 (The Grounding Walk)
Chapter 7, pages 192-193 ("Move Forward with Smart Program Upgrades")
Chapter 8, if you're interested in hiking and walking hills
Chapter 9, if you walk on the treadmill or indoors

What to review on DVD: Lesson Four: Let's Go Walking
Watch the DVD on the first workout of this week, if necessary

Program Development:
The Art of Journaling
Planning for Week 8

Write in the days and times for your 5 sessions this week:

Workout #1	Workout #2	Workout #3	Workout #4	Workout #5 The Grounding Walk
Day _____	Day _____	Day _____	Day _____	Day _____
Time _____	Time _____	Time _____	Time _____	Time _____

THEME OF THE WEEK

Moving Forward into New Terrain

In Weeks 7 and 8, we begin to turn the decision making process over to you so you can practice building your own personal program. This week, you'll be choosing your first four walks and be responsible for developing your own program, one that is sensitive to your current needs.

This week you'll still work on bringing together all your lessons and skills, but feel free to be adventurous by adding hills or quicker cadence, and tuning into what feels good. New terrain can mean anything from new types of grounds, to challenging surfaces, increase in steepness, different paces, or new environments, including off-road walking, hiking the hills, or stepping on a treadmill. This week is about options and tailoring your program to fit your needs, so decide which types of walks you want to do before the first workout and plan accordingly where you'd like to walk.

Not everyone, however, needs to walk hills, and not everyone needs to be on a treadmill. Your lifestyle, goals, and body will dictate what's best for you. Do you want to keep a well-rounded program for general good health? Are you training to accomplish a specific goal? Choose the walks and create a program that keeps you moving forward in the direction of your goals.

For example, if you're planning to hike a local mountain with your kids during a fall retreat, you'll need to build some hills into your weekly program to prepare yourself beforehand. By physically conditioning your body properly, you'll be able to enjoy that hike and make the most out of it. Similarly, if you want to walk a half marathon or marathon next year, you should start thinking about building your endurance, which can be helped, if necessary, with the use of a treadmill (especially during the cold winter months!).

This is where you're required to take Body Sensing to the next level. It is crucial that you listen carefully to what your body is telling you. By doing so, you'll find that the choices you make come from deep within and will be the choices that carry you toward your vision.

> *As you introduce a quicker pace or new terrain to your walking program, it is essential to focus on your form first and foremost. With good form, you can increase the intensity of your program without fear of injury.*
> *REMEMBER FORM COMES FIRST*
> *Faster walking or walking on more difficult terrain will come more easily with good walking technique.*

Non-Identification

(Pages 181-182 in the book)
It's much easier to stay with a program if you're not constantly judging yourself whether or not you're doing a good or bad job of things. In order to be the most helpful to yourself (and others you walk with), learn to remove yourself from identification with your body.

What does that mean? Just because you might feel uncomfortable while you're walking, doesn't mean that you should feel bad about yourself. Learning to not identify with your struggles is a huge step in sustaining a positive attitude with your walking program. When you're more objective with yourself, your assessments won't be strewn with judgments and self-inflicted reproachment.

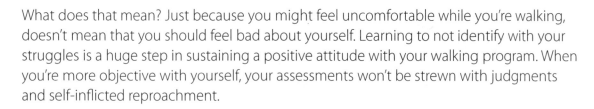

Lighten Up! Enjoy Yourself!

We're all human, and none of us moves perfectly, or stays on a program perfectly, or learns as quickly as we'd like to. But, no one needs to have road blocks… in any learning situation. And, negative judgments about yourself will only serve to slow down your learning process because you might be so busy focusing on what's wrong that you miss the lesson of how to do it right.

The mind is a tricky thing. One moment it can be your best friend, a neutral observer telling you what it sees going on, and the next minute it can be slicing you to ribbons. If you find yourself in the doubtful end of this spectrum, Make a Choice to go for the higher ground and don't pick up the phone if your lower voices are calling. Enough said?

WORKOUT #1

Today's Date: _____

LESSON: 5 MINUTES

• Watch Lesson 4 on the DVD: Let's Go Walking (if you need to)

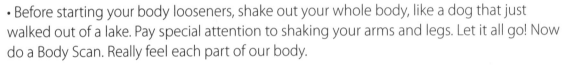

PRE-WALK BODY LOOSENERS: 5 Minutes

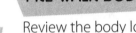

Review the body looseners on your DVD, or refer to the book *(pages 142-155)*. Do all of your looseners, finishing with the **Grounding Stance**.

• Before starting your body looseners, shake out your whole body, like a dog that just walked out of a lake. Pay special attention to shaking your arms and legs. Let it all go! Now do a Body Scan. Really feel each part of our body.

Then, do the following exercises:

• Ankle Rolls: Do 10 clockwise circles and then 10 counter-clockwise. Switch legs andrepeat the exercise.
• Knee Circles: Do 10 clockwise circles and then 10 counter-clockwise circles.
• Hip Circles: Do 10 clockwise circles and then 10 counter-clockwise circles.
• Sacrum Circles: Do 10 clockwise circles and then 10 counter-clockwise circles.
• Pelvic Rotations: Do a few rotations on each leg.
• Spine Rolls: Do 3 repeats.
• Spinal Twist: Do 3 repeats.
• Shoulders and Upper Back: Do 10 with right leg back, 10 with left leg back.
• **Grounding Stance**: Hold for 30-60 seconds.

MAKE A CHOICE!

Go back to the list of focuses. Review each pair of focuses you chose to practice for this walk. If you're unsure about any of the focuses, go back to the DVD and watch the section that covers the focus in question. Once you're clear on which focuses you'll be practicing, MAKE A CHOICE to concentrate on each of your chosen pairs of focuses during this walk. Follow the instructions below for help.

MOVE FORWARD INTO YOUR WALK: 25-40 MINUTES

Set your watch for 5-minute intervals. Grab your metronome and set your cadence to medium (60-65 spm).

FOCUSES DURING YOUR WALK:

• First 5 minutes: Warm up at a strolling pace. Practice your belly breathing. Try to get your breathing in synch with your strides.

• Next 20-35 minutes: Walk at a medium pace (60-65 spm) while alternating between the upper body focus and the lower body focus you chose. Start your countdown timer and go through your walk changing focuses every 5 minutes. Then, do both focuses together. Go back and repeat the same progression with the same focuses, or do the same progression with two new focuses. For a real challenge try to hold all 4 focuses in the last five minutes.

• Last 5 minutes: Cool down at a strolling pace. Feel the effects of your walk on your entire body—from head to toe.

POST WALK STRETCHES: 5 Minutes

Do your calf, achilles, hip flexor, hamstring, adductor, quadriceps, lats, and leg drains. Follow with the **grounding stance**.

✳ SEE YOU WHEN YOU GET BACK! ✳

END OF WALK REVIEW: 5 MINUTES

Welcome back. For six weeks we've been asking you questions for your End of Walk Review. Here we'll turn over the End of Walk Review to you and have you begin the practice of journaling.

The Art of Journaling

Journaling is an important part of maintaining a commitment to your ChiWalking program. It is one of the best tools to improve communications between your mind and your body. When you journal you can engage your body by Body Sensing and then writing down that experience…which is good use of your mind. By putting your thoughts and experience on paper, it gives you a chance to deepen your understanding and "relive" your walk in your mind.

A few tips:

• Body Sense before writing and feel your center. If you come from your center, you'll go much deeper with what is really happening for you.

• Write down whatever comes up. Have colored pens on hand if that helps. Let yourself express whatever is there.

• Ask yourself questions as if you were your own coach. Create solutions as if you are your own coach. (You can always refer back to the questions we've been asking).

• Do your writing after walking, and if possible, before you get into your next activity as your body will still be engaged and the experience will be fresh.

End of Walk Review

_____

_____

_____

_____

_____

_____

_____

_____

_____

_____

_____

_____

_____

_____

_____

_____

_____

_____

_____

_____

_____

Optional (for the first workout of the week):

Resting heart rate (RHR):_____beats per minute.

It is best to do this first thing in the morning.

FOCUSES IN BETWEEN WORKOUTS

Keep focusing on your Belly Breathing wherever you go. Also, check in so that you can find and feel your T12/L1 pivot point as frequently as possible.

RE-NEW YOUR COMMITMENT

I will do another ChiWalking workout on this day: _____
(Write this date down on your calendar or in any daily planner you keep.)

WORKOUT #2

Today's Date: _____

REVIEW: 5 MINUTES

Review whatever Form Focuses you want to work on.

PRE-WALK BODY LOOSENERS: 5 Minutes

(Review the DVD or pages 142-155 as needed.)

• Shake out your entire body from head to toe.

• Then do your ankle rolls, knee circles, hip circles, sacrum circles, pelvic rotations, spine rolls, spinal twists, shoulders and upper back, and grounding stance.

Take a moment to FEEL every piece of your body—inside and out.
Shake loose again if you like!

MAKE A CHOICE!

Take a few deep, belly breaths and think about the upcoming walk you've chosen for yourself on page 181 of this workbook. Or, do the Speed Workout suggested on the next page.

Review and revise, if necessary, the focuses you chose for this walk. Then make a choice to really work on all four focuses throughout your walk.

MOVE FORWARD INTO YOUR WALK: 25-40 MINUTES

Speed Workout

Set your watch for intervals and snap on that metronome. Remember: Your walk should reflect what your body, and not what your mind necessarily wants. The breakdown below is a guide to picking up your walking pace (i.e., speed work).

This is an introduction to faster walking.

FOCUSES DURING YOUR WALK:

• First 5 minutes: Warm up at a strolling pace (55-60 spm) and practice **belly breathing.**

• Next 15-20 minutes: Walk at a medium pace (60-65 spm) and practice your chosen focuses in 2, 3 or 5-minute intervals. Start with your upper body focus, then switch to lower body focus and then do both focuses together. Repeat the cycles until your time is up.

• Next 10 minutes: Walk at a faster pace (65-70+) while checking on your posture and form at every minute.

• Last 5 minutes: Cool down at a strolling pace. Focus on Belly Breathing.

POST WALK STRETCHES: 5 Minutes

Do your calf, achilles, hip flexor, hamstring, adductor, quadriceps, lats, and leg drains. Complete your stretches with a grounding stance before moving onto your next activity.

✳ SEE YOU WHEN YOU GET BACK! ✳

END OF WALK REVIEW: 5 MINUTES

Once you've cooled down, stretched and had a refreshing glass of water, spend a moment to do a body scan. Take your time and really body sense how your body feels after your workout. If you do this after every walk, you'll find that you actually get to enjoy each walk twice!

End of Walk Review

_____

_____

_____

_____

_____

_____

_____

_____

_____

_____

_____

_____

_____

_____

_____

_____

_____

_____

_____

_____

_____

_____

FOCUSES IN BETWEEN WORKOUTS

Remember the basics of getting into good posture:

- Get aligned and straighten your upper body
- Engage your core by leveling your pelvis
- Create Balance by tilting your statue and position your shoulders over your hips

Practice this whenever you can!!

RE-NEW YOUR COMMITMENT

I will do another ChiWalking workout on this day: _____.
(Write this date down on your calendar or in any daily planner you keep.)

WORKOUT #3

Today's Date: _____

REVIEW: 5 MINUTES

Practice whatever form focuses you're going to engage today

PRE-WALK BODY LOOSENERS: 5 Minutes

• Shake out your body!

• Do a Body Scan. Are you especially tight in any areas today? Let this be a call-out to the type of walk you choose today.

• Then do your ankle rolls, knee circles, hip circles, sacrum circles, and pelvic rotations, spine rolls, spinal twists, shoulders and upper body, and grounding stance.

> *Take two big Belly Breaths.*
> *FEEL your body once more. Relax any tension you feel.*
> *Then, step in front of a mirror and practice your arm swing.*

MOVE FORWARD INTO YOUR WALK: 30-40 MINUTES

Cardio Walk
A Cardio Workout is done in alternating intervals of fast and slow, which work and rest the heart. Approach each interval with the pinpointed concentration of an Olympic gymnast. Get your watch and metronome ready. Set your countdown timer to beep every 2 minutes.

FOCUSES DURING YOUR WALK:

• First 5 minutes: Warm up at a strolling pace (55-60 spm) and practice **belly breathing.**

• Next 20-35 minutes: Walk for 2 minutes at a fast pace (65-70 spm) followed by 2 minutes at a slower pace (60-65 spm). Change your focuses after every slow interval. Here's the order of your intervals: Do 1) **two upper body focuses**, then 2) **two lower body focuses**, then 3) **upper and lower focuses together**. Then, go back and repeat the same progression of focuses…

1. 2 min. fast upper body
   2 min. slow upper body

2. 2 min. fast lower body
   2 min. slow lower body

3. 2 min. fast upper and lower body
   2 min. slow upper and lower body

… repeat until your time runs out.

• This walk, as you can see, is designed to be as much an exercise for your mind as it is for your body. It is also designed to challenge your ability to be non-identified with what you are doing…and how well you are doing it. Have fun and don't take yourself too seriously.

POST WALK STRETCHES: 5 Minutes

Do your calf, achilles, hip flexor, hamstring, adductor, quadriceps, lats, and leg drains. Follow with the **Grounding Stance**.

✳ **SEE YOU WHEN YOU GET BACK!** ✳

END OF WALK REVIEW: 5 MINUTES

End of Walk Review

_____
_____
_____
_____
_____
_____
_____
_____
_____
_____
_____
_____
_____
_____
_____
_____
_____
_____
_____

RE-NEW YOUR COMMITMENT

_I will do another ChiWalking workout on this day: _____
(Write this date down on your calendar or in any daily planner you keep.)_

WORKOUT #4

Today's Date: _____

REVIEW: 5 MINUTES

Review whatever focuses you're working on

PRE-WALK BODY LOOSENERS: 5 Minutes

• Loosen up and shake out your body from head to toe.

• Then do your ankle rolls, knee circles, hip circles, sacrum circles, and pelvic rotations, spine rolls, spinal twists, shoulders and upper body, and grounding stance.

> *Take two big Belly Breaths.*
> *FEEL your body once more. Relax any tension you feel.*
> *Then, step in front of a mirror and practice your arms swing.*
> *Double-check your posture—including your head position.*
> *Do a Body Scan as you look in the mirror.*
> *Body sense for any tight areas and work to relax them during your body looseners and your walk.*

MAKE A CHOICE!

Think about the upcoming walk you've chosen for yourself on page 181 of this workbook. Review, and revise if necessary, the focuses you chose for this walk. Then make a choice to really work on all four focuses throughout your walk. Or, try the Aerobic/Long Walk described on the next page.

MOVE FORWARD INTO YOUR WALK: 45-60 MINUTES

Aerobic/Long Walk

This walk should be your longest walk each week and you can do it as often as desired. It is done at 55-70spm depending on your level of conditioning and should be done without stopping if possible. You should walk at a moderately fast pace, but not be out of breath. This walk is great for weight-management. Increase length as your conditioning allows. Perfect walk to practice your form focuses.

FOCUSES DURING YOUR WALK:

• First 5 minutes: Warm up at a strolling pace (55-60 spm) and practice your **belly breathing.**

• Next 35-50 minutes: Walk at a medium pace (60-65 spm) and practice your chosen focuses in 2, 3 or 5-minute intervals. Start with your **upper body focuses**, then switch to **lower body focuses** and then do **all focuses together**. Repeat these cycles until your time is up. If you're feeling any discomfort, see what you can do to adjust your technique.

• Last 5 minutes: Cool down at a strolling pace. Focus on Belly Breathing.

POST WALK STRETCHES: 5 Minutes

Do your calf, achilles, hip flexor, hamstring, adductor, quadriceps, lats stretches, and leg drains. Finish with the grounding stance.

When you increase your walking time to more than 30 minutes, your body will increasingly metabolize fat for fuel. The longer you walk, the higher percentage of fuel burned will be body fat.

✳ **SEE YOU WHEN YOU GET BACK!** ✳

END OF WALK REVIEW: 5 MINUTES

As soon as possible after the end of your walk, go to your journal and write down how your walk went, and any other notes of importance to you. It's a good way to take in all the value of what you just did.

_____

_____

_____

_____

_____

_____

_____

_____

_____

_____

_____

_____

_____

_____

FOCUSES IN BETWEEN WORKOUTS

Straighten your upper body whenever you're sitting…in your car, at dinner, at the office. Sitting is where most people's posture really falls apart, so it's a great place to practice.

RE-NEW YOUR COMMITMENT

I will do another ChiWalking workout on this day: _____
(Write this date down on your calendar or in any daily planner you keep.)

WORKOUT #5

Today's Date: _____

REVIEW: 5 MINUTES

• The Grounding Walk *(pgs. 123-124 in the book.)*

PRE-WALK BODY LOOSENERS: 5 Minutes

• Shake out your entire body and relax any tight areas.

• Do a Body Scan to make sure you're as loose as can be. If you can't loosen it all up, address this in your walk today.

• Do your ankle rolls, knee circles, hip circles, sacrum circles, and pelvic rotations, spine rolls, spinal twists, shoulders and upper back, and grounding stance.

MAKE A CHOICE!

Today you're going to do another walk from the ChiWalking Matrix: The Grounding Walk. A great time to do this walk is when you're feeling a little scattered and not particularly in touch with yourself. If most of your energy is stuck "upstairs" in your head, it's always a good idea to "lower your energy" and reinstate a sense of balance in your being. We all have moments when we want to escape from our minds, and that's exactly what this walk is designed to do.

MOVE FORWARD INTO YOUR WALK: 30-40 MINUTES

The Grounding Walk
Plan to spend at least 30 minutes in this walk, but increase that to a full 45 minutes if you're feeling great at 30 minutes and you have the time. Set the countdown timer on your watch for five-minute intervals so you stay mindful in the practice. Re-read pages 123-124 for complete directions. The Grounding Walk is about collecting yourself when you're feeling scattered and "outside" yourself.

FOCUSES DURING YOUR WALK:

• First 5 minutes: Begin with a Grounding Stance. Body Sense. Then walk at a relaxed pace on the slow side. Allow yourself to sink into the earth more than usual.

• Next 20-30 minutes: Continue your walk at a comfortable pace and focus on cycling energy through the lower half of your body. Pay close attention to your pelvis, legs, and feet for the full 20-30 minutes, if possible.

• Last 5-10 minutes: Cool down at a strolling pace and resolve to "pull the plug" on your mind anytime you feel the need to.

> *The Grounding Walk is great for clearing your mind*
> *and returning your attention—and Chi—back to your body.*

POST WALK STRETCHES: 5 Minutes

Do your calf, achilles, hip flexor, hamstring, adductor, quadriceps, lats stretches, and leg drains. Finish with the grounding stance.

✳ SEE YOU WHEN YOU GET BACK! ✳

END OF WALK REVIEW: 5 MINUTES

PROGRAM DEVELOPMENT: 15 MINUTES

Create your walks for Week 8
Go to Appendix A, Program Development, Week 7, Part 1.

Congratulations on finishing Week 7!
Take a moment to look back on your week
and sense how you feel inside and out, from your mind to your
muscles. Acknowledge to yourself all the good work
you put into your walking program
and think about what you learned this week.

FOCUSES IN BETWEEN WORKOUTS

Between now and your next workout, plan to stop at least twice a day to focus on
posture and form. Whenever you're walking, check on your **breathing**, and the **balance**
you create between your upper and lower body as you move forward. Move as a fluid
unit.

RE-NEW YOUR COMMITMENT

I will start Week 8 on this day: _____
(Write this date down on your calendar or in any daily planner you keep.)

WEEK 8 OVERVIEW

Theme of the Week: The Upward Spiral of Chi
Life Beyond the 8-Week Program

Chi-Skill: Consistency

Minimum Time Commitment: 5 workouts, 5 hours total

Body Looseners: Do them all!

5 Walks: Various paces, various terrains

1. 30-45 min. **Cardio Walk** alternating fast/slow cycles

2. 30-40 min. **Form Focus Walk**

3. 30-45 min. **Cardio Walk (or Hilly Walk)** alternating fast/slow cycles

4. 45-60 min. **Aerobic/Long Walk** repeating cycles of focuses

5. 40+ min. **The Chi-Gathering Walk**

Post Walk Stretches: All of them!

What to re-read in the book:
Chapter 2, pages 36-38 ("Move Forward")
Chapter 3, pages 55-59 ("Consistency")
Chapter 5, pages 116-123 ("The Chi-Gathering Walk")
Depending on your personal program, you may want to refer to Chapters 8 and 9.

What to re-view on DVD: Whatever you need help with.

Program Development:
• Smart Program Upgrades
• Beyond the workbook

Write in the days and times for your 5 sessions this week:

Workout #1	Workout #2	Workout #3	Workout #4	Workout #5
Day _____	Day _____	Day _____	Day _____	Day _____
Time _____	Time _____	Time _____	Time _____	Time _____

The Upward Spiral of Chi

As you Move Forward beyond this book, the lessons you'll discover on your own will help keep the chi flowing in your life—inside and outside of your workouts. Remember, as you integrate the inner focuses of ChiWalking into your life, your chi will flow increasingly through your body, and your life as a whole will Move Forward in an upward spiral. This upward movement allows you to make higher choices, which will ultimately result in a healthier, happier you.

Remember, one of the main ChiWalking Principles and laws of nature is Gradual Progress. Any process develops best when it happens gradually over time. Throughout the past several weeks we've been building your program gradually. Now it's time to revisit the theme of Gradual Progress in this last week, with regard to upgrading your program and keeping it fresh. Continue to review your goals, create new goals, and, let yourself enjoy the process.

This week you will create your own journal and walking program. First, go back and review the entries you made in earlier weeks. Which focuses were your most difficult? Which walks were the most challenging? When did you have the most fun? How would you gauge your fitness and energy levels now?

Use your answers to help you design a program. Use the Matrix in Appendix C, pg. 194 of this workbook, to choose appropriate walks that fulfill your fitness and energetic needs. How would you like to feel after your walk? Pick a walk that you are drawn to and see what happens.

You may find that you can change and direct your energy better than you ever thought possible.

Consistency

(Read pages 55-59 in the book)

When you maintain a consistent program, you'll reap more and more rewards because you'll be fueling that upward spiral of chi week after week, and year after year.

There are many things in life that require consistency. You know that brushing your teeth at least twice a day is a non-negotiable practice. You do it consistently no matter what. The same goes for eating, drinking, and getting a good night's sleep. By being consistent, you establish healthy habits. If you can achieve that same level of consistency with ChiWalking, you'll enhance your quality of life exponentially because, unlike much of those other activities you do routinely, ChiWalking will help your body, emotions, mind, and spirit all together. And, because you're introducing mindfulness into your life, it will make all other activities you do easier and more enjoyable.

This week, notice the things you do consistently that give you good energy and make you feel settled and positive. Notice aspects of nature that are consistent and give you an understanding of your world, from the sun setting and rising, to the seasons changing. When your walking program becomes a consistent part of your life, as it is for many people, you will build long-term health and energy. If you walk consistently with healthy moving habits, such as you've learned these past 8 weeks, it will have a positive effect on your whole person: mind, body and spirit.

WORKOUT #1

Today's Date: _____

LESSON: 15 MINUTES

• Go back and review any lesson on the DVD that you feel needs more of your attention.

PRE-WALK BODY LOOSENERS: 5 Minutes

You've already learned all the body looseners. Review them on your DVD if you need to, or refer to the book (*pages 142-155*).

Ankle rolls, knee circles, hip circles, sacrum circles, pelvic rotations, spine rolls, spinal twist, shoulders and upper back, ending with the grounding stance

Learn Post-Walk Stretches: *5 Minutes*

• Review your post-walk stretches (if you need to) by refering to Appendix B

Remember: You've learned all the stretching exercises now. Stretching is just as important as your walk, so make time for it. End your stretching session with the Grounding Stance before moving on to your next activity.

MAKE A CHOICE!

Do what you need to do to get ready for today's walk. If you want, look in the mirror and go through getting aligned, engaging your core and creating balance before choosing to start walking. Then, think about which walk you've chosen to do and which focuses you're going to work on. Now, make a choice to stay mindful in your practice for the duration of your walk.

MOVE FORWARD INTO YOUR WALK: 25-40 MINUTES

This is one of two Cardio Walks this week. Set up your countdown timer for the length of your intervals and your metronome at your fastest cadence. Go over this workout in your mind and think about what you'll be doing. Only use your metronome during your fast intervals. Slow down and rest in between. Review the focuses you'll be doing.

FOCUSES DURING YOUR WALK:

• First 5 minutes: _____

_____

• Next 20-35 minutes: _____

_____

_____

_____

• Last 5 minutes: _____

_____

POST WALK STRETCHES: 5 Minutes

Do your calf, achilles, hip flexor, hamstring, adductor, quadriceps, lats, and leg drains. Finish with the grounding stance.

✳ **SEE YOU WHEN YOU GET BACK!** ✳

END OF WALK REVIEW: 5 MINUTES

Write down your impressions, thoughts and observations.

_____

_____

_____

_____

_____

_____

_____

_____

_____

_____

_____

_____

_____

_____

Optional (for first workout of the week):

Resting heart rate (RHR): _____beats per minute.

FOCUSES IN BETWEEN WORKOUTS

Choose your own two focuses:

1) _____

2)_____

RE-NEW YOUR COMMITMENT:

My next workout will be at: _____(fill in the time)

on:_____ (fill in the day).
(Write this date down on your calendar or in any daily planner you keep.)

WORKOUT #2

Today's Date: _____

LESSON: 5 MINUTES

• Review any lesson you need to on the DVD.

PRE-WALK BODY LOOSENERS: 5 Minutes

(Review the DVD or pages 142-155 as needed.)
• Shake out your entire body from head to toe.

• Then, do your ankle rolls, knee circles, hip circles, sacrum circles, pelvic rotations, spine rolls, spinal twists, shoulders and upper back, and grounding stance

MAKE A CHOICE!

Once again, do what's necessary to prepare for today's walk. Take a few deep, belly breaths and think about the upcoming walk you've chosen. Make a choice to stay present in your mind every minute of the walk.

MOVE FORWARD INTO YOUR WALK: 30-40 MINUTES

Like before, set up your countdown timer or your metronome if you need to. Chart your walk in your mind and review which one you'll be doing. Write down the focuses for this walk below.

FOCUSES DURING YOUR WALK:

• First 5 minutes: _____

_____

• Next 20-35 minutes (include focuses): _____

_____

_____

_____

• Last 5 minutes: _____

_____

POST WALK STRETCHES: 5 Minutes

Do your calf, achilles, hip flexor, hamstring, adductor, quadriceps, lats, and leg drains. Complete your stretches with a grounding stance.

SEE YOU WHEN YOU GET BACK!

END OF WALK REVIEW: 5 MINUTES

Write down your impressions, thoughts and observations.

_____

_____

_____

_____

_____

_____

_____

_____

_____

_____

_____

_____

FOCUSES IN BETWEEN WORKOUTS

How well did you remember your chosen focuses since the last workout? Which ones do you want to focus on between now and your next workout? The same ones? Different ones?

1) _____

2)_____

RE-NEW YOUR COMMITMENT:

My next workout will be at: _____(fill in the time)

on:_____ (fill in the day).
(Write this date down on your calendar or in any daily planner you keep.)

WORKOUT #3

Today's Date: _____

REVEIW: 5 MINUTES   *(Optional if you want)*

- Any lesson
- Body Looseners for the week
- Post-Walk Stretches for the week

PRE-WALK BODY LOOSENERS: 5 Minutes

• Do your ankle rolls, knee circles, hip circles, sacrum circles, and pelvic rotations, spine rolls, spinal twists, shoulders and upper body. Follow with the grounding stance.

MAKE A CHOICE!

Shake out your body and do a Body Scan. Then, inhale deeply, taking in a few belly breaths. Think about which walk you've chosen to do and make a choice to stay present during every minute of the walk.

WORKOUT #3   WEEK 8 - UPWARD SPIRAL OF CHI

MOVE FORWARD INTO YOUR WALK: WALK 45-60 MINUTES

Aerobic Long/Walk
This is the second of two Cardio Walks this week. Set up your countdown timer for the length of your intervals and set your metronome at your fastest cadence. Go over this workout in your mind and review the focuses that you'll be doing. Only do your faster cadence during the faster intervals.

FOCUSES DURING YOUR WALK:

• First 5 minutes: _____

_____

• Next 20-35 minutes: _____

_____

_____

_____

• Last 5 minutes: _____

_____

POST WALK STRETCHES: 5 Minutes

Do your calf, achilles, hip flexor, hamstring, adductor, quadriceps, lats, and leg drains. Finish with the grounding stance.

✳ **SEE YOU WHEN YOU GET BACK!** ✳

END OF WALK REVIEW: 5 MINUTES

Write down your impressions, thoughts and observations.

_____

_____

_____

_____

_____

_____

_____

_____

_____

_____

_____

_____

_____

_____

FOCUSES IN BETWEEN WORKOUTS

Look at your notes and find which two focuses are most challenging for you. Make these your focuses in between workouts.

1) _____

2) _____

RE-NEW YOUR COMMITMENT

My next workout will be at: _____(fill in the time)

on:_____ (fill in the day).
(Write this date down on your calendar or in any daily planner you keep.)

WORKOUT #4

Today's Date: _____

REVIEW: 5 MINUTES *(Optional if you want)*

- Any lesson
- Body Looseners for the week
- Post-Walk Stretches for the week

PRE-WALK BODY LOOSENERS: 5 Minutes

• Do your ankle rolls, knee circles, hip circles, sacrum circles, and pelvic rotations, spine rolls, spinal twists, shoulders and upper body. Follow with the grounding stance.

MAKE A CHOICE!

Before beginning this walk, take time to do a thorough Body Scan from head to toe. Then, take three big belly breaths and give your body a good shake to loosen it up.

MOVE FORWARD INTO YOUR WALK: 45-60 MINUTES

Aerobic/Long Walk

The walk today is long and should be done at a comfortable, medium pace. Be sure to stay well hydrated. Take a water bottle with you if there are no regular water stops along your planned route. Dress suitably and set your countdown timer to beep every 10 minutes. When it goes off, do the following things:

1. Check your posture.

2. Take a sip from your water bottle.

3. Reinstate the focuses you're working on.

4. Do a body scan to check for any areas of discomfort (and make any necessary adjustments).

Call a friend to go with you. Having company always makes the time go faster.

FOCUSES DURING YOUR WALK:

• First 5 minutes: _____

_____

• Next 20-35 minutes: _____

_____

_____

_____

• Last 5 minutes: _____

_____

POST WALK STRETCHES: 5 Minutes

Do your calf, achilles, hip flexor, hamstring, adductor, quadriceps, lats, and leg drains. Finish with the grounding stance.

 **SEE YOU WHEN YOU GET BACK!**

END OF WALK REVIEW: 5 MINUTES

Write down your impressions, thoughts and observations.

_____
_____
_____
_____
_____
_____
_____
_____
_____
_____
_____
_____
_____

FOCUSES IN BETWEEN WORKOUTS

Pick two focuses that you consistently have the most difficulty remembering.

1) _____

2) _____

RE-NEW YOUR COMMITMENT

My next workout will be at: _____ *(fill in the time)*

on: _____ *(fill in the day).*
(Write this date down on your calendar or in any daily planner you keep.)

WORKOUT #5

Today's Date: _____

PRE-WALK BODY LOOSENERS: 5 Minutes

• Do a Body Scan to make sure you're as loose as can be.

• Do your ankle rolls, knee circles, hip circles, sacrum circles, and pelvic rotations, spine rolls, spinal twists, shoulders and upper back. Follow with a grounding stance.

MAKE A CHOICE!

The Chi-Gathering Walk 40+ Minutes
We end the workbook with our favorite walk. In the Chi-Gathering walk you'll learn the skill of taking in chi from the world around you. (Page 116 in the book). This walk is completely different from any of the other walks because it is not a linear walk where you're going out for a given distance or amount of time. It is instead, a walk where you follow whatever draws your attention. During this walk we ask you to make a choice to focus more on the impressions of Nature coming into you through your senses, and less on the specific objects you're looking at. The point of today's walk is to feed your senses on all that is delightful.

Let your senses guide you… and let your mind rest! Listen to sounds, look at colors and shapes, feel the breeze on your face or the ground underfoot, smell the aromas. This is an exercise strictly for the senses; so let them have their day.

• Plan to spend at least 40 minutes in this walk or as long as you'd like.

• Walk at a slow to medium pace.

• Get out into nature, preferably on a well-established path, a trail, or a neighborhood with streets away from main thoroughfares.

•This walk is best done alone or with a ChiWalking partner who agrees to do their own Chi-Gathering Walk with you… in silence.

FOCUSES DURING YOUR WALK:

Since this walk is more for the senses and spirit than the mind or the body, the focuses are of a different nature. Here are some focuses for making your Chi-Gathering Walk truly nourishing:

• The ChiWalking focus to remember is your posture, which should always be in your consciousness.

• As you stroll along let your eyes rest on whatever is of interest. There is no right or wrong, just whatever scene is drawing you in the moment. It may be the pattern in the bark of a tree, or the details of a flower, or the shape of the curve in a stream. As you walk, be aware of all of your senses working.

• The only thing we ask you not to do, is engage your mind… which will inevitably want to quantify, describe, count, or compare everything you see. Just watch and take in the chi, or energy from what you see, feel, hear, and smell.

• Train your eyes to see your surrounding world in three dimensions, rather than the flat two-dimensional canvas that can become our habit. Notice shapes, shadows and lighting that gives each object it's full shape. Let your eyes take in the full depth of your surroundings. If you feel like stopping and pausing, do so.

• When you feel saturated, and are done with your walk, take time to Body Sense before moving on. Choose to take that energy with you into your next activity.

> *Because of the revitalizing nature of this walk, we recommend you do this one at least once month. It's like hitting your own "refresh button."*

POST WALK STRETCHES: 5 Minutes

Do your calf, achilles, hip flexor, hamstring, adductor, quadriceps, lats, and leg drains. Finish with the grounding stance.

✳ **SEE YOU WHEN YOU GET BACK!** ✳

END OF WALK REVIEW: 5 MINUTES

Write down your impressions, thoughts and observations.

_____

_____

_____

_____

_____

_____

_____

_____

PROGRAM DEVELOPMENT: 15 MINUTES

Life Beyond This 8-Week Program
Go to Appendix A, Program Development, Week 8, Part 1

RE-NEW YOUR COMMITMENT

I will start Week 9 on this day: _____
(Write this date down on your calendar or in any daily planner you keep.)

Appendix A
Program Development Pages

PROGRAM DEVELOPMENT: 20 Minutes

CREATE A VISION
(Refer to pages 182 and 183 in the book for more information.)

The first step in creating your own personalized ChiWalking Program is getting you aligned with your vision. This is where you start to look at the big picture of your life—where you want to go and who you want to become in mind, body, and spirit. In future weeks, we'll help you create day-to-day plans for fulfilling this vision.

Remember what a Vision really means…

• A vision describes how you want to be.

• A vision looks at quality not quantity.

• A vision should contain guiding principles.

• A vision has less to do with form and more to do with energy.

• A vision is an expression of how you want to feel.

• A vision is process oriented, not goal oriented.

• A vision embodies the kind of energy you want to have in your every day life.

On the following pages you can respond to a few questions that will help you begin to craft your vision. (A sample vision statement appears on the opposing page.) Try to use language that's specific and special to you. Be positive and insightful. Shine a light into your deepest self so you can see—and realize—your fullest potential. Be bold: record what you're really thinking and hoping for yourself. What kind of a person would you like to become?

Read your vision regularly; it will help you through the day-to-day struggles.

Writing a personal vision is an important tool for creating a foundation for what you want to build and accomplish in your life. Having a well-written, vivid vision is like having the future pull you forward into itself. All good things start in our minds with our imaginings. Your vision will be a focal point in your ChiWalking program. You'll use it to carry you through the rough spots and roadblocks that may attempt to throw you off your program.

MY VISION STATEMENT

How would you like to feel when you wake up in the morning?

_____

_____

_____

How would you like to feel when you go to sleep at night?

_____

_____

_____

How would you like to feel from day-to-day?

_____

_____

_____

Write a simple statement that reflects how you see yourself one year from now.

_____

_____

_____

_____

Five years from now.

_____

_____

_____

_____

_____

_____

Katherine's Vision Statement

How would you like to feel when you wake up in the morning?

Alert. Refreshed. Spirited. Joyful.

How would you like to feel when you go to sleep at night?

Accomplished. Tired. Ready for bed. Like I've had a successful, fulfilling day.

How would you like to feel day-to-day?

Strong. Energized. Inspired. Full of life. Like I'm living in the moment. ALIVE!

Write a simple statement that reflects how you see yourself one year from now.

I'm even more physically fit and better at balancing work, play, and relaxation. I get a lot of inspiration from our clients and it's amazing to me how far we've come in spreading our Chi Principles around the world. I seem to learn something new to add to my repertoire of Chi skills every day. They expand my mind and refocus my energy.

Five years from now.

I've got a lot on my plate between raising Journey and running the business, but I always make time for myself and for practicing the Chi Principles in everything that I do. They get me though the hassles of the day. Stress is easy to manage. My mind-body connection is strong.

Ten years from now.

_____

_____

_____

_____

_____

Take a moment to imagine reaching these goals. Try to feel these goals realized in your current body. Now, describe in a few words how it would feel physically and emotionally to live at that level of health and fitness. Be as specific as possible about all the benefits of looking and feeling great.

_____

_____

_____

_____

_____

My vision of what I want in an exercise program is:

_____

_____

_____

_____

_____

Use your vision statement as a sword against any negative voices that try to hijack your mind. Return to your vision statement whenever you need to remind yourself of where you want to go and what you want to accomplish.

Ten years from now.

I haven't slowed down a bit. I feel at my peak in my mid 50s, I'm feeling great and enjoying being so fit and healthy that I still go on adventurous trips with my husband and our teenage daughter. I'm at total peace within myself and can be emotionally, physically, and mentally present every minute of the day with whomever I'm communicating. I continue to inspire others to start a walking program and achieve their own inner peace. I feel balanced, able to conquer anything. I have a heightened sense of self and confidence.

Take a moment to imagine reaching these goals. Try to feel these goals realized in your current body. Now, describe in a few words how it would feel physically and emotionally to live at that level of health and fitness. Be as specific as possible about all the benefits of looking and feeling great.

Utterly amazing. Indescribable. As if I'm "lucky." I envision people telling me that I look "great." They say I'm vibrant, carry a healthy glow, youthful, haven't skipped a beat, and am happy no matter what. Everything about me is balanced and aligned—in mind, body, and spirit.

My vision of what I want in an exercise program is:

A program that fits my life, can be sustained, and brings me rewards that are physical, mental, emotional and metaphysical. It challenges me to the core and nourishes my body for lifelong health.

PROGRAM DEVELOPMENT: 10 Minutes

Review and Refine your Vision

Go back to the Vision statement you wrote in your last workout and see if there's anything you want to change or add. Here are some additional questions to ask yourself:

- Does your vision statement reflect who you are and what you want?

- Is your vision aligned with who you want to be? Try to weed out other people's ideas of who you SHOULD be.

- Do you have an overall feeling for your vision? Spend a few minutes quietly and imagine your vision being your reality. Sense what it would feel like to be living your vision.

- Read your vision anytime you feel discouraged or frustrated…it will help keep you on track and moving forward.

With your vision clearly in mind, you can do anything!

PROGRAM DEVELOPMENT: 15 Minutes

Your Physical Assessment

(Review pages 184-186 in the ChiRunning book, entitled,
"Get Aligned with Where You're at Today".)

Today we'll do a physical assessment. Tomorrow you'll assess your attitude. So let's get to it. This will give you a picture of your "starting point." (Honesty is the best policy here; no one has to read any of this!) Just think: You can look back on these pages at the end of the eight weeks and see how far you've come. You can't change your age, of course, but you can change just about everything else.

> *Use Caution!! Consult with a health care practitioner before starting any physical fitness program. If you have any current mitigating health-related factors, make an appointment to see your health care practitioner. Share your intentions and goals, and get a thorough physical. Don't be afraid to ask questions and address any health issues you have.*

Basic Info:

Age:_____

Weight:_____

How would you rate your overall health and energy level? Write a personal assessment of your overall health.

_____

_____

_____

_____

How much exercise do you get, on average, per week? What kind of exercise, if any, do you do?

_____

_____

_____

_____

At what time during the day do you feel the most energetic and alert? _____

At what time during the day do you feel the least energetic and alert? _____

Do you have any health concerns or issues that might impact your walking program? If so, list them here.

_____

_____

_____

_____

Do you have aches or pains or feel restricted in your movement anywhere? Write down the specifics.

_____

_____

_____

_____

How does writing this down make you feel? Inspired to make changes? Uncomfortable? Surprised by your answers?

_____

_____

_____

_____

_____

Taking the time to give an honest assessment of your physical health is a great way to keep you moving toward better health. Write anything else of importance to you.

_____

_____

_____

_____

_____

Assess Your Attitude

(Refer to page 186 in the book for background material.)

As you know, your mindset and your attitude can make all the difference to your health and your day. Here, we'll assess the various aspects of your self that can help in learning and implementing ChiWalking, and those that might hold you back. For those that impede your progress, you'll do some brainstorming to stop those negative voices before they take hold.

If journaling is new to you, this might be a challenge at the start. Putting your attitude to paper is a GREAT, self-benefiting experience that will give you some tools for making the most out of your program.

How would you describe your general attitude? Happy and optimistic? Pessimistic? A bit of both? Write down an assessment of your general attitude.

_____

_____

_____

_____

_____

What qualities or characteristics do you possess that will enhance your walking program? For example, are you goal-oriented? Have strong willpower? Are you ambitious and easily inspired? Are you feeling inspired and ready to commit to your fitness program? Write down all your internal allies.

_____

_____

_____

_____

_____

What qualities or characteristics may jeopardize your walking program? For example, do negative-sounding voices stream into your mind and set you back? Do you find yourself giving excuses instead of participating in a physical activity? Do you procrastinate a lot? Write down anything that might impede your progress.

_____
_____
_____
_____
_____
_____

What mental voices have pulled you back in the past? What one-liners have derailed your fitness program in the past? Think of some of them and write them down.

1._____

2._____

3._____

4._____

5._____

What can you say to yourself instead of the above statmenst to get you back on track?

1._____

2._____

3._____

4._____

5._____

Examples of Common One-liners:

1. "I'm tired and I've got too much to do."

2. "I don't feel up to it; and I'd rather sit on the couch and watch TV."

3. "I'll do it tomorrow."

How to Conquer Them:

1. *A walk will invigorate me and make me feel like a million bucks.*

2. *I'll be able to work more efficiently once I get my walk in.*

3. *Think how accomplished I will feel when I do a walk today and take it to a new level tomorrow!*

Check in on Your Vision: 2 minutes

• Reread your Vision Statement you wrote last week and remember what it is your working toward. Feel your potential!

PROGRAM DEVELOPMENT: 15 Minutes

Physical Goals

As part of "engaging your core," you have the opportunity to move forward from a place deep within yourself and from your deepest source of power. Now is a good time to create personal goals that reinforce and honor your vision. (Re-read pages 187-189 for inspiration.) Take a moment to write down some physical goals you have.

Write down your physical goals here:

1._____

2._____

3._____

4._____

5._____

stronger body
healthy heart
weight loss
specific distance
more energy
more flexibility

Emotional Goals

Emotional goals can be a bit more difficult to create than physical goals. It might be easier to say you want to lose 10 pounds or feel more energized during the day than affirming that you want more inner balance in your life and greater esteem. We all have emotional goals in our mind, but we don't always write them down or stick them to the refrigerators as reminders. Well, push any hesitations aside because you're going to write whatever you want––no one will read it. Be true to yourself and really think about which emotional goals mean the most to you. Write down what is most meaningful for you.

Write down your emotional goals here:

1._____

2._____

3._____

4._____

5._____

lower stress

heightened self awareness

let go of anger

enthusiasm

calmness

connect with others

emotional balance

be centered

feel joy

PROGRAM DEVELOPMENT: 15 Minutes

Mental Goals

Now that you have some physical and emotional goals written down, let's complete your goal-setting project by recording a few mental and metaphysical goals. (See pages 188-189 for more info.) Remember: Be honest and self-challenging! Go back and re-read your vision statement to spark some ideas. Consider what goals you need to make in order bring your vision into your life.

Remember: Mental goals revolve around the use of your mind and your essential mind-body connection. Metaphysical goals include anything in your life that has an inward or invisible quality.

Write down your mental goals here:

1._____

2._____

3._____

4._____

5._____

think positively
challenge my mind
get organized
learn to focus
improve memory
remember details

Metaphysical Goals

Take your time here. Don't rush your thinking. Decide which goals, in particular, reflect you and your vision. (Don't limit yourself to these if you've got a handful waiting to spill out onto the page.) If you have a hard time coming up with any of these, don't pressure yourself. You can always come back and fill these pages in later when those goals do come to mind. Your emotional and metaphysical goals work most powerfully when they come from inside YOU.

Write down your metaphysical goals here:

1._____

2._____

3._____

4._____

5._____

be in the present
appreciate life
be centered
experience oneness
non-identification

PROGRAM DEVELOPMENT: 10 Minutes

Create a Balanced Program

Building a balanced program starts with knowing what works for you. With your goals in mind, think about how you can design a schedule that fits your lifestyle and current responsibilities.

Look back at the personal assessment and the goals you wrote down last week. Using those notes you can begin to create your own tailor-made program that will guide you toward achieving those goals as well as your long-term vision for yourself. Re-read pages 189-191 in the book for a refresher if haven't done so already.

First, choose the number of days you intend to walk.
Second, schedule those workouts into your week to best ensure they will happen.

Check which days work for you and fill in the chart:

BEST DAYS TO WALK	BEST TIME	LENGTH OF TOTAL WORKOUT
MONDAY		
TUESDAY		
WEDNESDAY		
THURSDAY		
FRIDAY		
SATURDAY		
SUNDAY		

The schedule you come up with doesn't have to be perfect the first time through. Consider it a "work in progress" that might go through many changes until you settle with a program that consistently works for you, week in…week out.

PROGRAM DEVELOPMENT: 5 Minutes

Review & Rework Vision and Self-Assessment

It's been a while since you've written your vision statement. Time to go back and see if you want to make any revisions. You're more likely to stick to your program if you continually update your vision, goals, and assessment so it reflects where you are today—not yesterday. This will further help you bring you to where you want to be tomorrow.

On this day, go back and review your vision and self assessment from Weeks 1 and 2.

Ask yourself:

• Does your vision meet your current hopes and expectations?_____

_____

_____

_____

• Do you need to add any more language to your vision that further hones in on what you want and where you want to go?

_____

_____

_____

_____

_____

_____

_____

• Has anything about your personal assessment changed?

_____

_____

_____

_____

_____

• How would you rate your overall health and energy level now as compared to when you started?

_____

_____

_____

_____

• How has your attitude changed since you made that assessment in Week 2?

_____

_____

_____

_____

• Have any negative mental voices been bothering you lately? If so, what are they?

_____

_____

_____

_____

• How can you combat these negative voices through positive reinforcement?

_____

_____

_____

_____

• Finally, what's the one thing in your vision that you think about the most—and that drives you to make the most out of your days?

_____

_____

_____

_____

_____

PROGRAM DEVELOPMENT: 5 Minutes

Consider Walking with a Buddy

Creating balance in your weekly program, and staying on top of your vision, goals, and program development can be easier with a buddy. You can provide extra support and inspiration for each other. Up till now, you may have been doing your walks alone, which is optimal for focusing on your posture and form, and mastering the Chi-Skills and Principles. A buddy can help you move toward realizing your goals and ultimately, your vision. Of course, it will help to choose someone who's also practicing the ChiWalking method.

If you haven't found a partner to work with, visit www.chiwalking.com and find a group near you.

PROGRAM DEVELOPMENT: 5 Minutes

Choosing Your Own Focuses for Your Walks

This week you'll begin choosing which focuses you'd like to practice during your walks. You've just finished doing your 20minute-walking test. That's the first walk of the week. There are four walks remaining, the last of which will be dedicated to learning a new walk from the ChiWalking Matrix (Appendix C). The 3 walks in the "middle" of your week will be geared towards helping you to "put it all together" as the theme of the week implies. So, in this section of program development, you'll need to choose which focuses you'll be practicing during your next three walks. Pick one or two pairs of focuses for each walk. Choose one focus from the upper body list and one focus from the lower body list. Write down the pairs of focuses you selected in the space provided and follow the instructions given for each of the next three walks. We've provided a list of possible focuses from which to choose. Choose a variety, and choose areas that need the most practice.

Upper Body Focuses:	**Lower Body Focuses:**
Swing arms to the rear	Pelvic rotation
Relaxed shoulders	Relaxed lower legs
Proper head position	Legs swing to the rear
Chin tucked	Knees straighten to the rear
Upper spine straightened	Heels lift over your opposite ankle
Tilt the statue	Hips over ankles with each foot plant
Twisting at the Pivot Point	Feet and legs pointed forward
Belly breathing	Landing on the front of your heel
Elbows bent according to cadence	Ankles relaxed at all times
Relaxed hands	Pelvis level

Workout #2:

1st Set of focuses:

Upper Body _____ Lower Body_____

2nd Set of focuses (optional)

Upper Body_____ Lower Body_____

Workout #3:

1st Set of focuses:

Upper Body _____ Lower Body_____

2nd Set of focuses (optional)

Upper Body_____ Lower Body_____

Workout #4:

1st Set of focuses:

Upper Body _____ Lower Body_____

2nd Set of focuses (optional)

Upper Body_____ Lower Body_____

Refer back to this list and remember the chosen focuses before heading out for each of your next three walks.

PROGRAM DEVELOPMENT: 15 Minutes

Choose your Walks and Focuses for Week 7

We'll now create your walking program for Week 7. This is something you'll be doing regularly to keep your fitness program moving forward. Here is an outline of how to go about creating your own weekly schedule. You can choose walks from the Matrix (Appendix C in this workbook or on page 137 in the book). Some of your walks will be just like those we've been doing for weeks, wherein you choose focuses and practice them at intervals. These walks are called Form Focus walks.

The program has brought you to a 5-day-a-week walking schedule, which is the minimum you want to do if walking is your primary source of fitness. You can walk up to seven days per week, especially if you Create Balance in your program and in your movement.

The Ideal 5-day Walking Week

• One Aerobic/Long Walk (work up to 45+ minutes, no maximum) which is your longest walk of the week, holding your cadence at a contact 60-70 spm.

• One or two Cardio Walks (30-40 minutes maximum). See Week 7, page 129 in this workbook or page 103 in the book to learn this walk.

• One or two Form Interval Walks (30 minutes minimum, no maximum). These are the walks you've been doing all throughout this workbook where you choose Form Focuses and practice them in intervals. The pace is medium to fast paced (65-75 spm). Isolate the parts of your technique that need the most work. Our two most highly recommended focuses are: level your pelvis (to build core strength) and twist at your pivot point (T12/L1) to rotate your pelvis and relax your lower back.

• One other walk to manage your energy or to just have fun such as:

The Energizing Walk - See Week 6, pg. 113, in this workbook or pg. 125 in the book.

The Calming Walk – See Week 4, pg. 72 in this workbook or pg. 129 in the book.

The Grounding Walk – See Week 7, pg. 135 in this workbook or pg. 123 in the book.

The Chi-Gathering Walk – See Week 8, pg. 153 in this workbook or pg. 116 in the book.

More walks can be found on the ChiWalking Matrix (Appendix C or page 137 of the book).

Below, you'll choose the walks you'd like to do next week. And, just as you did at the beginning of this week, you'll be choosing the focuses you'd like to practice during each of those walks.

There are five walks in Week 7. There is extra space in case you want to do more than five walks. Or, choose from the Matrix (Appendix C). We offer suggested walks below.

After you've decided which walks you'll be doing, pick two focuses for each walk. Choose one from the upper body list and one from the lower body list. Pick the focuses you feel you need more work on and write down the pairs of focuses you choose in the space provided. You can also select a second set of focuses per walk if you'd like. Here's a list of possible focuses from which to choose:

Upper Body Focuses:	**Lower Body Focuses:**
Swing arms to the rear	Pelvic rotation
Relaxed shoulders	Relaxed lower legs
Proper head position	Legs swing to the rear
Chin tucked	Knees straighten to the rear
Upper spine straightened	Heels lift over your opposite ankle
Tilt the statue	Hips over ankles with each foot plant
Twisting at the Pivot Point	Feet and legs pointed forward
Belly breathing	Landing on the front of your heel
Elbows bent according to cadence	Ankles relaxed at all times
Relaxed hands	Pelvis level

Note: Suggested walks are in parentheses

Workout #1: Walk (Form Focus) _____

1st Set of focuses:

Upper Body _____ Lower Body_____

2nd Set of focuses (optional)

Upper Body_____ Lower Body_____

Workout #2: Walk (Speed Workout)_____

1st Set of focuses:

Upper Body _____ Lower Body_____

2nd Set of focuses (optional)

Workout #3: Walk (Cardio Walk)_____

1st Set of focuses:

Upper Body _____ Lower Body_____

2nd Set of focuses (optional)

Upper Body_____ Lower Body_____

Workout #4: Walk (Aerobic/Long Walk) _____

1st Set of focuses:

Upper Body _____ Lower Body_____

2nd Set of focuses (optional)

Upper Body_____ Lower Body_____

Workout #5: Walk (Grounding Walk)_____

1st Set of focuses:

Upper Body _____ Lower Body_____

2nd Set of focuses (optional)

Upper Body_____ Lower Body_____

Workout #6: Walk _____

1st Set of focuses:

Upper Body _____ Lower Body_____

2nd Set of focuses (optional)

Upper Body_____ Lower Body_____

Review the walk and focuses you've chosen before heading out.

PROGRAM DEVELOPMENT: 5 Minutes

Create Your Walks for Week 8

There are five walks in Week 8, the fifth walk will be dedicated to learning the Chi-Gathering Walk from the Matrix.

We added space if you want to do more than a total of 5 walks. We also included suggested walks for each workout.

After you've decided which walks you'll be doing, pick two focuses for each walk… one from the upper body list and one from the lower body list. Pick the focuses you feel you need more work on and write down the pairs of focuses you choose in the space provided. You can also choose a second set of focuses per walk if you'd like. Here's a list of possible focuses from which to choose:

Upper Body Focuses:	Lower Body Focuses:
Swing arms to the rear	Pelvic rotation
Relaxed shoulders	Relaxed lower legs
Proper head position	Legs swing to the rear
Chin tucked	Knees straighten to the rear
Upper spine straightened	Heels lift over your opposite ankle
Tilt the statue	Hips over ankles with each foot plant
Twisting at the Pivot Point	Feet and legs pointed forward
Belly breathing	Landing on the front of your heel
Elbows bent according to cadence	Ankles relaxed at all times
Relaxed hands	Pelvis level

Review the walk and focuses you've chosen before heading out.

Note: Suggested walks are in parentheses.

Workout #1: Walk (Cardio Walk)_____

1st Set of focuses:

Upper Body _____ Lower Body_____

2nd Set of focuses (optional)

Upper Body_____ Lower Body_____

Workout #2: Walk (Form Focus Walk)_____

1st Set of focuses:

Upper Body _____ Lower Body_____

2nd Set of focuses (optional)

Upper Body_____ Lower Body_____

Workout #3: Walk (Hilly Walk)_____

1st Set of focuses:

Upper Body _____ Lower Body_____

2nd Set of focuses (optional)

Upper Body_____ Lower Body_____

Workout #4: Walk (Aerobic/Long Walk)_____

1st Set of focuses:

Upper Body _____ Lower Body_____

2nd Set of focuses (optional)

Upper Body_____ Lower Body_____

Workout #5: Wlak (Chi-Gathering Walk)_____

1st Set of focuses:

Upper Body _____ Lower Body_____

2nd Set of focuses (optional)

Upper Body_____ Lower Body_____

Workout #6: Walk_____

1st Set of focuses:

Upper Body _____ Lower Body_____

2nd Set of focuses (optional)

Upper Body_____ Lower Body_____

PROGRAM DEVELOPMENT: 15 Minutes

Life Beyond This 8-Week Program

Until now, you've been doing a lot of journaling in this workbook, which has hopefully served to keep you active and engaged with your walking program. But what happens once you finish these eight weeks and you're on your own? You can always come back to this workbook to remind yourself of the lessons and reread the notes you've taken. You can prepare for your journey beyond these eight weeks by getting a journal or walking log to keep your momentum going. Make it your personal journal that follows your progress, your walks, your thoughts, goals, and vision, your health status, your realizations, whatever *you* choose to record.

Set up your first week (week 9) to revisit your overall program and make any necessary changes to your goals, vision, and personal assessment. Start by setting aside a section in your journal to record your assessments. Create a template you can repeat monthly, and include space to record the following:

- **Date**

- **Weight**

- **Resting Heart Rate**

- **Vision**

- **Physical goals**

- **Emotional goals**

- **Mental goals**

- **Metaphysical goals**

Next, create a weekly schedule for yourself:

BEST DAYS TO WALK:	BEST TIME:	LENGTH OF TOTAL WORKOUT:
MONDAY		
TUESDAY		
WEDNESDAY		
THURSDAY		
FRIDAY		
SATURDAY		
SUNDAY		

Pick a specific day of the week and make an appointment with yourself to sit with your journal and write down your walking schedule for the week ahead. Include what is appropriate for the week, and get your journal set up for making your entries.

Make room for writing down the focuses you plan to work on each week. Choose as many as you like and practice them in 1, 2, or 5-minute intervals during your walks.

Here are some additional ideas for ways to prepare your journal each week:

• If possible, after every walk, write down what focuses you were working on and how you are doing with that specific focus.

• In your last entry for the week, do an end-of-week review. Record how your week went overall. Was it great? Difficult? Easy and fun? A lot of work?

• Make room for writing down feelings, realizations, breakthroughs, difficulties or mistakes.

• Have a section reserved for writing down diet-related notes. Write down foods that you eat that seem to affect you and your walking program positively and negatively.

• Observe the ways your walking is affecting the rest of your life.

Again, these are guidelines. Choose what is most appropriate for you and get your journal ready for personal entries. Remember, this is your journal so you can use it for whatever you like!

Smart Program Upgrade

Once in a while, you will find it invigorating to take a time-out from your usual "routine" and consider how you can take your program to genuinely new heights. Revisit your vision, goals, and personal assessment about once a month. You can do this at the start of your first workout or at the end of your last workout of the week. It's up to you. But, if you feel the need to upgrade anything in your program, don't wait until the end of the month to do so. Upgrade your program when necessary and in a way that is healthy for your body.

Ask yourself the following questions:
Is my body ready for more…
      …time on certain walks?
      …days per week of walking?
      …challenging walks (more hills, steeper hills, faster cadence, trails,
           longer distances, training for a walking event)

No one can know your body better than you, so take the time to answer these questions as accurately and as honestly as you can. If you feel the need to change one or more of your walks, remember the Principle of Gradual Progress and add in your upgrades slowly over time, allowing your body the transition time to take on more.

It's okay to schedule walks that are more intense than others, but create consistency in your patterns. For example, alternate your workouts between easy terrain/moderate paces, and more challenging terrain/faster paces. This will prevent "burn-out" and keep you on your journey.

Appendix B
STRETCHES

Stretching

Here are the stretches referred to in this workbook. We don't generally recommend you stretch before walking because it is too easy to pull a muscle when your body is not warmed up. To insure that all of your stretching is safe for you, follow these simple rules:

• Begin each stretch by doing it lightly and slowly. Hold it for a few seconds and go more deeply into it as your body allows. Don't bounce when you stretch or you could pull a muscle.

• Relax and breathe out as you initiate each stretch.

• Begin stretching within ten minutes after ending your walk, while your muscles are still warm.

• If you've never done a stretch before, read the instruction very carefully and make sure you understand what to do. Stretch lightly after your first few walks until you become more comfortable with the stretching positions and the sequence.

CALF STRETCH

Stand about two shoe-lengths away from a wall or a chair and lean forward keeping your heels on the ground and your knees locked. Hold for ten seconds and repeat three times.

Calf stretch: Keep your heel down

ACHILLES STRETCH

Same position as the Calf Stretch, except that you are bending your knees as you lean into the wall or chair. Hold for ten seconds and repeat three times.

Achilles stretch: Bend your knee and keep your heel down

HIP FLEXOR & UPPER HAMSTRING STRETCH

Rest one foot on the top of something that is knee-height and move your pelvis toward the heel that is raised. Hold for ten seconds and repeat three times on each leg. Keep your trunk vertical. For an even better hip flexor stretch, lock the elbow of the arm that is on the same side of your body as the foot that is on the ground and extend it over your head as you press your pelvis towards your elevated heel. When your hip flexor feels like it's at a maximum stretch, arch your extended arm across your body and twist your upper body in the same direction. Hold for 30 seconds and repeat on the opposite side. This is a great stretch for the psoas.

Psoas stretch: hip flexor stretch with upper body twist

HAMSTRING STRETCH

Hamstring Stretch: Place one heel on something that is hip-height (knee-level is ok if you can't get your foot hip-height). Keeping both knees straight and your spine straight, bend at your hips and let your trunk fall towards your raised leg. Bend over only as far as your hamstrings allow. Hold for 20 seconds and repeat twice on each leg. You can also do this stretch sitting on the ground with your legs extended out in front of your body.

Hamstring stretch: Bend forward at the hips

ADDUCTOR STRETCH

Sit on the ground with your knees straight and your feet spread as far apart as possible. Bending at the hip and holding your spine straight, try to touch the toes on one foot for 20 seconds and then the other foot for 20 seconds

Adductor stretch: Bend towards each foot

QUADS STRETCH

With one foot on the ground, grab the ankle of your opposite leg with your hand and pull up on your heel. If you need to, you can stabilize yourself by holding onto a chair. Keep your knees together and pull your heel close to your butt. Gain additional stretch by leveling your pelvis while holding your foot.

Quadriceps stretch: For a better stretch, hold your knees together and level your pelvis.

Latissimus dorsi (LATS) STRETCH:

This stretches the back muscles just below your shoulder-blades. Stand tall, with your feet spread a little more than hip-width apart. Take one arm and reach over your head and grab that wrist with your opposite hand. Pull down on the crossed arm for 20 seconds, then repeat on the other side.

Lats stretch: Pull down with your lower arm

LEG DRAIN

Lie on your back with your feet propped up on a wall or chair. Let yourself relax in this position for 3-5 minutes before getting up. I often use the time to also do my end-of-walk review.

Leg drains: Feet up for 3 minutes

APPENDIX C - THE CHIWALKING MATRIX

(see pg 137 in the ChiWalking Book)

WALK TYPE	TO...	BOOK PG.	WKBK PG.	FREQUENCY	DURATION (MINS.)	CADENCE (SPM)	PACE	% MHR
Cardio	Strengthen your heart	103	129	Once a week/ same day	30-40	70-80	Alternate fast/easy	70-80
Aerobic/ Long Walk	Improve aerobic capacity and metabolize fat	106	132	As desired	60+	60-70	Moderate	55-70
Hilly	Build upper body & leg strength	108	106	As desired, but not on consecutive days	30-45	60-70	Moderate	60-75
Loosening	Loosen your muscles & joints while relaxing your entire body	113	N/A	Up to daily-- great at lunchtime	30-35	55-65	Very easy	50-65
Upper-Body	Strengthen & tone your shoulders & arms	115	N/A	As desired, but not on consecutive days	30-45	65-70	Moderate	55-70
Chi-Gathering	Gather chi energy into your body	116	153	As desired	60+	55-65	Very slow	50-65
Grounding	Collect yourself when feeling scattered & "outside" yourself	123	135	As desired	30-45	55-65	Very easy	50-65
Energizing	Increase flow of chi through your body	125	113	As desired... early morning best	30-45	60-70	Moderate	60-70
Focusing	Focus and direct your mind	126	91	As desired... early morning best	30-45	60-70	Moderate	60-70
Calming	Calm your mind & relax your body	129	72	As desired	30-45	55-65	Very easy	50-65
Meditation	Focus & quiet your mind	132	N/A	As desired	20-30	55-65	Very slow	50-65
Racewallking	Satisfy your need for speed	134	N/A	As desired	60+	70-80	Fast	70-80

Congratulations! You've completed your 8-week program.
Take a moment to look back on how far you've come. The past eight weeks
have hopefully been the launch pad to a lifelong practice of healthy choices.
So, just as you've been doing for the past 8 weeks, get your calendar out
and plan next week's walks.

All of us at ChiLiving wish you
the very best with your ChiWalking program.
By being consistent with your walking, you'll ensure yourself
a lifetime of vibrant energy and good health.

For additional support with your ChiWalking program
visit our website at www.chiwalking.com
or call toll-free 1-866-327-7867

Notes

Notes

Notes

Notes

Notes

Notes

Notes

Notes

Notes